Contents

CHAPTER 1

Setting the scene

SECTION A

The human footprint

The quality of the Earth's physical environment is of crucial concern to us all. It provides the natural life-support systems upon which we depend. It has a major impact on our health, living standards and general well-being. But the environment is fragile. It is easily damaged by human activities through pollution and many other forms of abuse.

There is a reciprocal relationship between living things and the environment (**1.1**). Over millions of years of evolution, a broad balance has been achieved between the two. In geologically 'recent' times, however, the growing presence of people has been the trigger for environmental change, disturbing that critical balance. This has been increasingly the case during the last 250 years, when the environment has been modified to the point of detriment. Throughout most of the world, it is now common to find environments bearing the scars of people. Humans have disturbed 90 per cent of the Earth's land surface to a greater or lesser extent. It is hard to find any areas of truly 'natural wilderness' untouched by human activity.

Figure 1.1 The Earth's natural systems

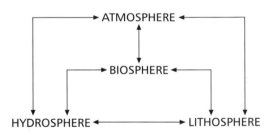

The severity of the human impact on the environment has increased as population numbers have soared. This explosive growth was made possible by advances in technology and the spread of economic activities. But both advances have by themselves caused much environmental damage. In a time-span of only a few thousand years, the human race has evolved from a primitive hunting and gathering state to today's highly urbanised and industrial society in which waste and pollution are very much the by-products. There is increasing evidence, however, that the environment can no longer sustain current levels of human activity.

Significant changes to the environment began around 10 000 years ago with:

- the discovery of fire
- the domestication of livestock
- the development of cultivated crops
- the building of permanent settlements.

The human population explosion that followed has had dramatic consequences for the Earth's natural systems: its climatic zones, ecosystems and species, coasts and rivers, as well as the processes that link them. The impact of economic development, and the disorder that comes with it, are destabilising complex systems that have taken hundreds of millions of years to evolve. They are upsetting the fragile natural balance. In 1987, the Brundtland Report (entitled 'Our Common Future') commented that '... while the Earth's natural systems function together in harmony, the human world is disordered and disjointed'.

One major impact has been on the **carbon cycle** (1.2). Huge areas of forest have been felled, and this has removed an important 'carbon trap'. The process of **photosynthesis** in green plants locks up huge quantities of carbon dioxide (CO_2) from the atmosphere. The fossil fuels (coal, oil and natural gas) are the remains of plants and animals that lived millions of years ago, and they store huge quantities of carbon. It is also stored in carbonate rocks, such as chalk and limestone, that accumulated on the beds of lakes and seas. When these fuels and other organic materials are burnt, they produce heat which is used for power and many other purposes. But as they burn, carbon dioxide and other pollutants are released into the atmosphere. The same applies when carbonate rocks are used by industry, for example in the manufacture of iron and steel.

Figure 1.2 The Earth's carbon stores

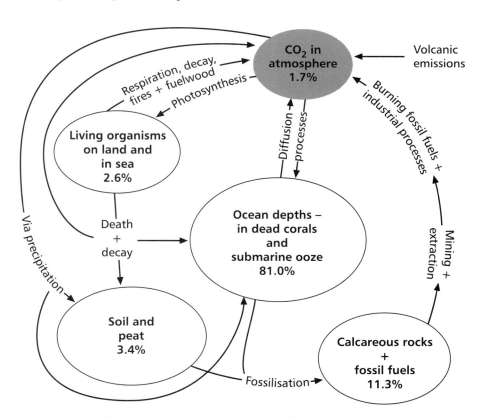

The severity of environmental degradation differs from place to place, often depending on the levels of development and population pressure. It tends to be the more affluent and 'developed' nations that are placing excessive and unsustainable demands on the environment and its resources. Ironically, such demands may actually have their greatest effects on the poorest members of the global community and in the least-developed countries. In a sense, environmental problems are being 'exported'. Many less-developed societies once lived in harmony with their environment. Their customs and ways of life actually sustained the ecosystems on which they depended. Few examples of such societies can be found today. Instead we find ourselves in an increasingly urban world. Massive rural–urban migration is concentrating not just people, but their environmental impact, particularly pollution. At the same time, in order to grow, towns and cities need to tap resources that lie outside their boundaries. All too often, such exploitation pays little or no regard to the environmental impact or future stocks.

In the industrially-advanced nations (the MEDCs), rapid population growth and the problems of urban expansion are now largely under control, but this has still to be achieved in many large, developing countries (the LEDCs) like Brazil, India and Mexico. It is often the case that environmental standards are lower and pollution controls less strictly enforced in LEDCs than in the MEDCs. Multinational enterprises (MNEs) may try to 'benefit' from this by establishing potentially polluting factories in such locations. It is a case of the rich exporting dirty, 'polluting technology' to the poorer nations. Production and pollution control costs are higher in the MEDCs because the **polluter pays principle** is more widely implemented; controls are more stringent and the penalties more severe if legal pollution limits are exceeded.

Pollution incidents in industrial areas of poorer countries (including the former Soviet countries) tend to be both frequent and serious. There have been several major accidents due to inadequate funding and poor attention to environmental safety. Examples include the Chernobyl nuclear power station disaster in 1986 and the Union Carbide accident in Bhopal (India) in 1984.

Case study: Industrial pollution accident at Bhopal, India

One of the world's worst industrial pollution incidents occurred in India in December 1984, when 40 tonnes of a highly toxic gas known as MIC (metho-isocyanate) leaked from the American-owned Union Carbide plant in Bhopal. At least 2500 people were killed by this cyanide-based gas, and the accident has caused persistent and continuing health problems to as many as 25 000 people. It has taken many years for the company to agree and provide compensation to all the people affected, and many claim that the amounts offered are 'paltry and totally inadequate'.

Union Carbide has not been accused of deliberately operating pollution control standards that were lower than they would have been in the USA. However, the accident may well reflect much poorer supervision by staff and a lack of safety training. It may also be a reflection of India's rapid drive for industrial expansion in order to find employment for its rapidly growing population. In this race for economic survival, environmental protection has been given a low priority.

Review

1 Which of the advances given in the bullet points on page 4 do you think has had the greatest impact on the natural environment? Give your reasons.

2 Explain what is meant by the **carbon cycle**.

3 Do you think that MEDCs deliberately 'dump' polluting industry and waste on LEDCs? Justify your argument with supporting examples.

4 Explain the link between environmental abuse and:
   a the level of development
   b the level of population pressure.

The nature of pollution

Figure 1.3 Types of pollution

Pollution is said to occur when the quality of the environment is disturbed, impaired, degraded or contaminated in some way. Chemicals cause most pollution (**1.3**). Gases, liquids and solids released in sufficient quantities into the environment by people will certainly cause damage of some kind.

Indicators of chemical pollution in the environment are:

- visible amounts of the chemical and strong odours
- harm caused to animals and plants (both domestic and wild)
- human health disorders that, in extreme cases, put life at risk
- damage to monuments and buildings through staining and decay of building stone.

Our perception of pollution should be extended beyond chemicals to include **aesthetic pollution**. This has three components, namely **noise pollution** (excessive or unwanted sound and vibration), **visual pollution** and **olfactory pollution** (smell). Since 'beauty is in the eye of the beholder', what is thought to constitute aesthetic pollution will depend very much on the individual. It will also be strongly influenced by current fashions and trends in the society in which the person lives. Because of its subjective nature, the assessment of aesthetic pollution, particularly visual pollution, can easily become a controversial matter.

Pollution can have far-reaching and damaging effects on all parts of the Earth's physical environment (**1.1**):

- **The atmosphere** – air quality can be seriously impaired by smoke and by a wide range of pollutant gases.
- **The hydrosphere** – water in all its forms and locations within the hydrological cycle (groundwater stores, rivers, lakes, the seas and oceans, and even rain, snow and ice) can be contaminated by pollutants held in solution or suspension.
- **The lithosphere** – land and its surface-covering of soil may be poisoned by pollutants such as acid rain, fertilisers and pesticides from agriculture, together with toxic chemicals from industry, mining and landfill sites. A landscape can also be spoiled aesthetically by unsightly development and excessive noise.
- **The biosphere** – life on Earth may be modified or killed, and its health damaged, by all forms of pollution.

Although it is convenient for us to look at these parts of the environment separately, it is important to understand that in practice they do not function independently. Each 'sphere' interacts with all the others, and so do different pollutants, whatever their source (**1.1**). For example, industry and motor vehicles release various pollutants into the atmosphere, including sulphur dioxide, oxides of nitrogen and particulate matter. Poor air quality aggravates, if not causes, lung diseases in people. Those same pollutants also cause the **acid deposition** that adversely affects buildings, rivers, lakes and water supplies. Equally, this acid deposition can bring about the death of lichens, trees and other wildlife, with knock-on effects on grazing animals.

Pollution has a greater impact on some physical environments and natural systems than others, and on particular parts of systems. Once they have been released into the environment, chemical pollutants follow particular **pathways** and become concentrated in particular places or parts of a system. Such places are called **pollution sinks**, and it is here that the impacts of pollutants are at their most apparent. For example, artificial fertilisers consisting of soluble nitrates and phosphates are applied to agricultural land. These are leached from the soil or run off the surface, eventually entering water-courses such as ditches and streams. They become concentrated in these places by evaporation, especially during droughts and hot weather. As water percolates down through the soil and pervious bedrock, the pollutants will also enter groundwater stores. In this way, water-courses and groundwater stores become pollution sinks.

In both cases, high concentrations of artificial nutrients may cause environmental problems. A particular problem for water-bodies on the surface is **eutrophication**. Large amounts of nutrient cause an excessive growth of aquatic plants and algae. Eventually these die, and huge amounts of oxygen are required from the water as they decay. If the **biochemical oxygen demand** (**BOD**) exceeds the amount of dissolved oxygen available in the water, there will be knock-on effects that cause the death of fish and other aquatic organisms.

It is possible to measure and monitor the amount of pollution in a system. Types of pollutant can be identified and their sources can often be traced back and attributed. Remedial courses of action can be quite simple. But it all takes time and money, as well as commitment. The sad fact is that usually pollution most affects the poor – and the poor are hardly in a position to call for pollution control.

Case study: Pollution in Delhi

Delhi is India's political capital. It has also been designated India's 'pollution capital' (see **2.6** on page 17). Indeed, it has the dubious distinction of being ranked as the fourth most polluted city in the world.

Delhi demonstrates the impacts of pollution in all its forms. For this reason, the city will figure not only in this particular case study, but also in several of the following chapters. Remember, however, that the different forms of pollution interact with each other, and in such a way as to degrade the overall quality of the environment and cause severe health disorders.

Delhi suffers from:

- poor air quality – at times it is near to being toxic, due to huge emissions from industries and motor vehicle exhausts

- foul water courses contaminated by discharges of raw sewage together with domestic and industrial waste
- noise levels that are near-deafening in many places
- slums and poorly maintained buildings, many of which are unsightly in the extreme.

The city's poverty, severe overcrowding, substandard housing and poor levels of healthcare further exacerbate the many problems caused by pollution.

Review

5 Create a matrix table, with 'Types of pollution' heading the rows and the 'The Earth's four spheres' heading the columns. For each box, suggest an appropriate example.

6 Distinguish between **pollution pathways** and **pollution sinks**.

7 Write an essay on 'The poor and pollution'.

8 To what extent do you agree with the statement: 'Pollution is an inevitable cost of development'?

SECTION C

Other forms of environmental abuse

Pollution is only one example of human abuse or misuse of the environment. There are many other ways in which people physically alter the natural world and disrupt natural systems. The fragile environment depends on many finely-balanced mechanisms. Any intervention, no matter how slight, will trigger a series of repercussions. Well-intentioned attempts to reduce the likelihood of a major disaster such as a flood, or to protect land and property from coastal erosion, can have unintended consequences. Those consequences can be just as serious as the threat that triggered the intervention in the first place.

We would therefore be justified in saying that any human action that involves the natural environment and natural systems is going to result, to a lesser or greater degree, in some form of environmental abuse. In other words, it is impossible to use the natural environment and its resources without inflicting some form of damaging change. That is a vital message to be remembered at all times, particularly in all matters to do with development. We need to discover and adopt forms of development that minimise the human impact on the environment. **Sustainability** must be our watch-word.

9 Make a list of as many different forms of environmental abuse as you can think of. Are you able to assemble them into some sort of classification?

10 Explain what **natural systems** are. List the ways in which people can modify them to reduce the threats posed by natural hazards.

11 'Human activities in one area may have unintended, but nevertheless serious, consequences for another.' Illustrate this statement.

12 Explain what is meant by **sustainability**.

13 Make a list of ways in which you might make your own life-style more environmentally sustainable.

Enquiry

1 From the Internet, collect information about pollution in a British city. Write an account that:
- identifies the types of pollution and their sources
- shows how each type threatens the environment
- examines attempts made to reduce pollution levels.

2 What were the causes and consequences of the Chernobyl nuclear power station disaster of 1986?

3 Suggest ways of assessing the **quality of the environment**.

Air pollution

Sources of trouble

Pollution of the Earth's atmosphere reduces the quality of the very air we breathe. Atmospheric pollution is known to:

- cause health problems in people, including asthma and other breathing disorders
- kill or damage plant and animal life
- deplete the **ozone layer**
- cause **acid rain**.

There is also strong evidence to suggest that air pollution is a cause of recent **global warming** and therefore is likely to have serious and long-term effects on climate.

Examples of natural pollutants in the air include the fumes and dust emitted by volcanic eruptions, and smoke from spontaneous forest fires. But most air pollution has human origins:

- burning fuelwood and fossil fuels for power, cooking, heating and lighting
- emissions from many industrial processes such as metal smelting
- gases produced by livestock and by agricultural practices
- exhaust fumes from transport
- radioactive fallout.

The circulation of the Earth's atmosphere moves air pollutants from one place to another. Even in such remote places as Antarctica, pollutants that must have had their origins in faraway industrial regions have been found in recently formed ice.

Figure 2.1 Primary air pollutants in the UK (1994)

	% of total weight
Carbon monoxide	39
Sulphur dioxide	22
Nitrogen oxides	18
Volatile organic compounds	18
Black smoke (suspended particulate matter)	3

Figure 2.2 Main sources of air pollutants in the UK (1994)

	% of total weight
Road transport	41.0
Power stations	20.5
Domestic	8.0
Others	30.5

	% of total weight				
	Carbon monoxide	Sulphur dioxide	Nitrogen oxides	VOCs	Black smoke
Road transport	89	2	49	33	59
Power stations	0	65	24	0	4
Domestic	6	3	3	2	22
Others	5	30	24	65	15
Weight (m tonnes)	4.8	2.7	2.2	2.2	0.4

Figure 2.3 Analysis of air pollutant sources in the UK (1994)

Figure **2.1** shows the main ingredients of polluted air in the UK. Figure **2.2** indicates the activities that release them and **2.3** the percentages and quantities involved. You should note that carbon dioxide (CO_2) has been omitted from these tables as it does not contribute directly to pollution. However, huge amounts of CO_2 are released into the atmosphere making it *the* most important of the greenhouse gases – see also **2.9** and **2.10**.

Although human activities produce hundreds of different air pollutants, they fall into two main groups: gases and particulates.

Gases

- **Carbon monoxide** (CO) is formed by burning carbon-based fuels in car engines, power stations and central heating boilers.
- **Carbon dioxide** (CO_2) is given off when any organic materials (including fossil fuels) are burnt. It is the chief **greenhouse gas**.
- **Sulphur dioxide** (SO_2) is released when 'sour' fossil fuels are burnt. Vehicle exhaust fumes, emissions from power stations and industry are the main sources. It is the chief ingredient of **smog** and **acid rain**.
- **Nitrogen oxides** (NO_x) form when fossil fuels are burnt at high temperatures, especially in vehicles and power stations. These gases react with water vapour and add to acid rain; they also help to form photochemical smog.
- **Volatile organic compounds** (VOCs) are mainly hydrocarbons that form gases or droplets at normal air temperatures. Some, like methane, are produced during natural processes such as digestion in animals and decay of plants. Others are released into the air in vehicle exhaust fumes and by industrial processes.

Particulates

This second group of air pollutants are all measured under the heading:

■ **Suspended particulate matter** (SPM) – microscopic solid particles and droplets of liquid. Solid SPM includes carbon particles (soot and black smoke), pollen, dust and various metals, including lead. Liquid SPM consists of droplets of acids (mainly sulphuric), various pesticides, hydrocarbons (derived from oil) and polychlorinated-biphenyls (PCBs).

Review

1 Why is there concern about pollution of the atmosphere?

2 Consider your school buildings and the various activities that take place there. List the ways that they are adding to air pollution: **a** directly and **b** indirectly.

3 Study **2.1** to **2.3** and the information about air pollutants.
   a What are the problems associated with NO_x and SO_2 as air pollutants?
   b Which of the UK's sources of air pollutants are most likely to be causing the problems of acid deposition experienced by Scandinavia?
   c What are the alternatives to producing energy from fossil fuels? Which do you consider would make the greatest contribution to reducing environmental problems?

SECTION B

An historical perspective

Air pollution by people dates back to the first use of fire. However, it was the discovery of coal as a fuel source that greatly increased air pollution problems. There have been attempts to stop air pollution in towns in England since the 13th century. Royal proclamations were issued at that time which aimed to put a stop to '… the excessive burning of "sea coal" because of … the great public nuisance caused by the large amounts of soot and sulphurous smoke in the air'. However, pollution from coal-burning persisted in London and other large British cities, even though offenders risked torture.

The Industrial Revolution, first in Britain and later in Europe and the USA, led to the establishment of many coal-burning factories. The industrial cities, most of them located on coalfields, were characterised by their soot and strong gaseous smells from sulphur dioxide, nitrogen oxides and other toxic emissions. Buildings were blackened, washing hung out to dry was soon covered with smuts, and people's health suffered (**2.4**).

Figure 2.4 A typical British industrial city in the nineteenth century

Once the railways had been constructed, coal fires became the main means of heating homes in nearly all parts of Britain, and the steam trains themselves were significant burners of coal. Victorian London was notorious for its frequent 'pea-soupers' – choking, yellow smoke-fogs that caused many health problems and deaths. Later they became known as 'coal smogs'. It is no surprise, therefore, that a trip to London in those days became known disparagingly as 'going to the Smoke'.

Case study: The London smog of 1952

London's air pollution problems increased during the first half of the 20th century as fumes from bus, lorry and car exhausts were added to the coal smoke from steam trains, homes, factories and power stations.

In December 1952, the pollution culminated in the infamous **smog**, which was responsible for the deaths of over 4000 people. Wind-speeds dropped to zero and fog formed as an anticyclone settled over Britain. The descending air caused a temperature inversion that prevented any escape of the smoke and fumes from the London Basin. A blanket of choking smog extended for nearly 50 km across London, from the Chiltern Hills to the North Downs. As you descended from the hills and entered the smog, it was like passing from day into night.

For five days the smog got thicker and thicker. It was soon so dense that Londoners literally could not see a hand in front of them. They found their way from place to place by groping along fences, walls and buildings. Buses had to be led through the streets by someone walking in front with a flaming torch! There was so much sulphur dioxide in the fumes mixing with the fog that the droplets became almost pure sulphuric acid. One estimate put the pH value as low as 1.6! It was essential to wear a 'smog mask' over the mouth and nose so that the acidic fumes and soot were not inhaled.

In order to solve the smog problem, the UK Government drew up new legislation. The Clean Air Act of 1956 prohibited coal-burning in many of Britain's urban areas. London's air has become much cleaner as a result, and 'pea-souper' smogs have been largely eliminated. The amount of sunshine recorded in Britain's towns and cities has risen sharply as coal-burning has declined.

Today, however, a different kind of smog is encountered in many urban areas. Cities as far apart as Los Angeles, Mexico City, Athens, Delhi and Tokyo, all suffer from **photochemical fog** or **haze**. It occurs during hot, anticyclonic weather in air heavily polluted by vehicle exhaust fumes. Still air and strong sunlight are necessary to trigger the reactions between various chemicals released in vehicle exhaust fumes. These reactions give rise to tiny visible particles that form this kind of smog.

Case study: Smog in Los Angeles

The huge sprawling city of Los Angeles in California, the USA's 'Sunshine State', covers an area of some 4000 km². It is located in a huge basin bordered by the San Gabriel and San Bernadino Mountains.

Los Angeles has been called 'Automobile City'. There is little public transport. Its scattered suburbs are connected by a complex network of freeways that criss-cross the landscape like a tangled mass of concrete spaghetti. The combination of Los Angeles' geographical location, its heavy dependence on the motor car, and anticyclonic weather, gives rise to an enormous environmental problem – photochemical smog.

Figure 2.5 How photochemical smog is formed

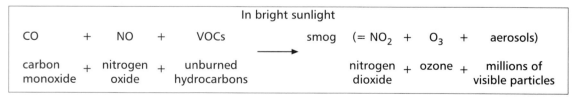

Los Angeles' 5.5 million cars burn 45 million litres of petroleum a day. The surrounding hills and the frequent temperature inversions associated with sinking anticyclonic air help trap the noxious exhaust fumes released by the cars (2.5). Gentle westerly breezes blowing across the cold Californian Current just offshore increase the effects of the temperature inversion.

The resulting photochemical smog causes stinging eyes and aggravates lung problems, including asthma and bronchitis. On bad days, Los

Angeles' TV and radio networks issue health warnings. People are urged not to exercise out of doors, and the very young and very old are told to stay indoors. In recent years Los Angeles' smog problem has been considerably reduced by what are claimed to be the world's toughest anti-pollution laws.

Case study: Air pollution in Delhi

Each day Delhi's three million vehicles release around 1990 tonnes of pollutants into the atmosphere. *The Hindu*, one of India's leading daily newspapers, describes the belching fumes and the noise generated as creating 'a living hell'. India is an LEDC and the vast majority of its huge population have a low income and poor living standards. Thus, most of the vehicles on Delhi's potholed roads are badly maintained and run on poor-quality fuel. Overloaded lorries, crammed buses, taxis, private cars, auto-rickshaws (with 2-stroke engines, running on low-quality kerosene), motor cycles and scooters crawl along in low gear. Traffic congestion is so severe that speeds seldom exceed 20 km/h. Roughly 65 per cent of Delhi's air pollutants come from motor vehicles. Unregulated industrial development is another major source, being responsible for about 25 per cent.

Much of the air pollution from Delhi's motor vehicles is in the form of suspended particulate matter: a measure of 460 micrograms of SPM per cubic metre of air is 'average' for Delhi. This is well in excess of the World Health Organisation's prescribed 'safe limit' of 200 micrograms per cubic metre. At busy traffic intersections, SPM levels often reach well over 1000 micrograms per cubic metre.

Figure 2.6 Geographical influences on the development of air pollution in Delhi

As many as five million Delhi residents suffer from breathing disorders of varying severity. These range from mild wheezing, through persistent nagging coughs, to severe asthmatic attacks and chronic bronchitis. During 1995 and 1996, acute bronchitis cases in Delhi increased by 23 per cent. The city had the highest proportion of asthma cases in India, with 40 per cent of the child population affected. In 1996 alone, more than 7000 people in Delhi were reported to have died from acute asthma. The true figure was probably much higher, as the cause of death often goes undiagnosed and unreported. Doctors claim that the choking air pollution is also a major factor in other illnesses, including eye, throat, liver and skin disorders, heart disease, kidney failure, thyroid gland problems and cancer.

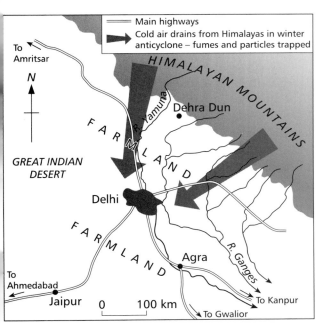

However, the amount of air pollution and its impact varies in different parts of the city, and at different times of the year (**2.6**). People living in Delhi's slum areas, and especially those adjacent to main roads, experience the greatest amounts of pollution. As a consequence, they suffer more damage to their health than the better-off living in less-crowded suburban areas. The young and the old are also more vulnerable to the effects of air pollution than the rest of the population.

Review

4 Identify the similarities and differences between coal-smoke (London-type) smog and photochemical smog (Los Angeles-type), paying particular attention to their formation.

5 What were 'pea-soupers'? Why have they become a thing of the past?

6 What are the consequences for human health of high levels of air pollution in Delhi?

SECTION C

The problem of acid rain

Figure 2.7 Damage to vegetation caused by acid rain

Acid deposition involves SO_2, NO_x and SPM. SPM may also fall to the ground as solid particles or **dry deposition**, but if it dissolves in water it is known as **wet deposition** or **acid rain**. Acid rain is by no means a recent discovery; Robert Smith, a pollution inspector in Manchester, first used the term in the 19th century. Acid rain has a pH of less than 5.6.

Consequences

Acid deposition harms vegetation, water life, buildings and historic monuments. Many lichen species are particularly sensitive to the presence of sulphur, and the types and amount growing on trees and other hard surfaces are useful indicators of air quality. The down-wind pollution pattern from, say, a power station or factory can often be traced by mapping the distribution of certain lichen species. Their absence indicates the most heavily polluted areas.

Huge areas of forest and the ecosystems of thousands of lakes in Norway and Sweden have been degraded and damaged by acid rain. At least 10 per cent of Sweden's 40 000 lakes are now too acidic to support fish life; another 18 000 are partly acidic. Much of the acid deposition in Scandinavia has been carried by the prevailing winds from sources in the UK.

Damage by acid rain often shows up in forest surveys (2.7). In Europe, oak trees are known to be declining throughout their range because acid rain is disrupting the nutrient balance of soils. Potassium and calcium are leached out and the remaining aluminium and manganese inhibit root growth and cause foliage damage. Over three-quarters of Europe's oak trees show at least some damage to their crown foliage. Indications that trees are under stress from acid deposition include:

- discoloured leaves and premature leaf fall
- loss of roots
- die-back and abnormal growth of branches, especially in conifers
- death of ground-cover vegetation beneath trees
- increased amounts of fungal infections and disease.

Prevention

The best line of attack would be to prevent the acid rain from forming in the first place. Prevention would mean stopping sulphur and NO_x emissions – but how? Acid deposition is a global problem, for which global solutions are required. There have been a number of international conventions and initiatives seeking to reduce emissions. Recent examples include the inter-governmental Climate Change Conference at Kyoto in 1997 and its follow-up in Buenos Aires in 1998. Although the main concern of these conferences was to agree global reductions in greenhouse gases, the scope for cutting levels of sulphur and NO_x was also examined.

There are several ways in which acid-forming emissions can be reduced:

- Decrease the amounts of fossil fuels used for energy production by developing alternative energy sources (HEP, solar, geothermal, wind, wave and tidal power). Nuclear power also reduces toxic emissions but, of course, creates other environmental risks.
- Ban the use of fuels with a high sulphur content. This would mean, for example, drastically cutting the use of sulphur-rich lignite, which is widely used in the former East Germany and Poland.
- Use natural gas and low-sulphur crude oil. For example, North Sea oil has an average sulphur content of only 1.5 per cent compared with the 3.5 per cent or more in some Middle Eastern oilfields.
- Cut the amounts of sulphur in coal to be burnt in power stations by crushing and washing the fuel before use. This can halve sulphur content, but the technique increases the risk of water pollution.
- 'Scrub' (de-sulphurise) flue gases emitted from fossil-fuel-burning power stations, metal smelters, brick kilns and the like.
- Fit catalytic converters to cars to cut down amounts of unburned hydrocarbons and NO_x gases in car exhaust fumes. Converters are now compulsory on all new cars sold in the EU.

Most MEDCs now have regulations designed to limit their output of SO_2 and other sulphur compounds. Power stations, oil refineries, chemical plants, natural gasfields and production plants are fitted with 'scrubbing' equipment to remove sulphur, either during the actual production process or from the 'tail gases' emitted from the chimneys of processing plants. But in poorer countries, there is still a long way to go.

If acid rain cannot be prevented from forming and falling, are there ways of reducing its effects? Attempts have been made in Scandinavia and Germany by applying lime to affected lakes and forests to neutralise the acidity. In some areas with large conifer plantations, such as mid-Wales and the Southern Uplands of Scotland, the problem has been reduced a little by interspersing conifer planting with broad-leaved trees. These produce a more neutral leaf litter.

Review

7 What do you understand by the term **acid deposition**?

8 In what ways does acid deposition damage environmental quality?

9 What kind of international agreements do you think are necessary if the problems of acid deposition are to be solved?

SECTION D

Global warming

The Earth has experienced many climatic changes during its 4600 million-year history. Perhaps the most spectacular in recent geological time was the Ice Age of the Pleistocene period. It lasted around a million years. The glaciers finally retreated from the British Isles only 10 000–15 000 years ago. Since then, there have been several minor fluctuations in climate, with warmer, cooler, wetter and drier episodes. In the second half of the 20th century, increasing evidence accumulated of a marked, general **global warming**, which most scientists and decision-makers now regard as a matter of fact. The Meteorological Office and the Inter-governmental Panel on Climatic Change (IPCC) predict that between the years 1990 and 2010, global temperatures will experience an average rise of between 1.5°C and 4.5°C.

Causes

Many explanations have been suggested for long-term climatic change. They include:

- continental drifting
- periods of intense volcanic activity
- showers of meteorites
- the Earth wobbling on its axis
- a temporary increase in the ellipticity of the Earth's orbit around the Sun
- variations in sunspot activity.

In recent years, however, scientists have been pointing the finger at human activities as the current cause of climatic change. It is increasingly apparent that air pollution is to blame. Some polluting gases released into the atmosphere are creating a **greenhouse effect** and it is this that may be leading to **global warming**.

When coal, oil, natural gas (the fossil fuels) and other organic materials are burnt, the process of photosynthesis is, in effect, reversed. The energy that has been stored ever since their formation is released, along with CO_2. Since 1860, the CO_2 content of the atmosphere has gone up by nearly 75 per cent, with the global total reaching 6056 million tonnes in 1995.

In 1997, the UK alone released some 149 million tonnes of CO_2 into the atmosphere, about 2.4 per cent of the global total for the year. Like other MEDCs, it emits about twice as much CO_2 per head as the global average. The sources and quantities are shown in **2.8**. In recent years, emissions from power stations have dipped sharply with the switch from coal to gas and nuclear power, but those from road transport have increased sharply.

Figure 2.8 Sources of carbon dioxide emissions in the UK, 1970 and 1997

Source	1970 Amount (m tonnes)	1970 % of total	1997 Amount (m tonnes)	1997 % of total
Power stations	57	31	40	27
Industry	66	36	37	25
Transport	22	12	37	25
Domestic	26	14	23	16
Offices	11	7	12	7
Total	**182**		**149**	

Figure 2.9 The relative direct contributions to global warming from UK emissions of greenhouse gases

Greenhouse gas	% of total weight
Carbon dioxide	87.0
Methane	8.0
Nitrous oxide	4.4
Other	0.6

Carbon dioxide makes up by far the largest proportion of greenhouse gases released into the atmosphere (**2.9**). The others are:

■ **Methane** – molecule for molecule, methane is far more powerful than CO_2 as a greenhouse gas. It is released by the decay of organic material such as rubbish dumped in landfill sites, by livestock (especially cattle) as a by-product of their digestive processes, and by some coal mines.

- **Nitrous oxide** (NO_x) – released by catalytic converters fitted to car exhausts.
- **CFCs** (chlorofluorocarbons) – until recently used as a propellant in aerosol sprays, a coolant liquid in refrigerators, freezers and air conditioners, and in the manufacture of some kinds of fast-food packaging.

Figure 2.10 The workings of the greenhouse effect

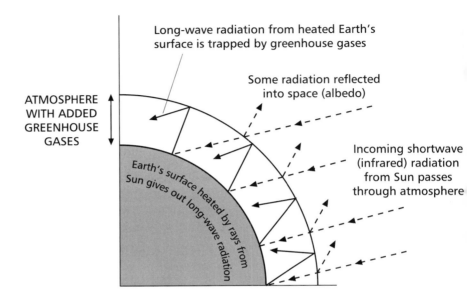

Greenhouse gases allow the short-wave heat energy radiated by the Sun to pass through the atmosphere until it reaches the Earth's surface (**2.10**). However, the gases absorb the long-wave heat energy being radiated back from the Earth. Thus they act in a similar way to glass trapping heat in a greenhouse. The heat so trapped may well be responsible for a general rise in atmospheric temperatures.

The fallout of dark-coloured SPM from polluted air blowing over and settling on ice sheets and snowfields may be another factor. The dark colour reduces the reflectivity (the **albedo**) of the ice and increases heat absorption. The greenhouse effect may also be made worse by widespread forest destruction. With fewer trees available to use CO_2 in the process of photosynthesis, less carbon is being locked up and stored as organic material.

Consequences

If global warming is a fact, the increase in temperature is likely to trigger a cascade of knock-on effects.

- Thermal expansion of water in the seas and oceans will raise sea-levels
- Mountain glaciers and the Greenland ice cap will melt, thereby also raising sea-levels. Fortunately, satellite observations reveal that there has been relatively little melting of the Antarctic ice sheet so far.

- Rising sea-levels will threaten the livelihoods and the lives of many millions of people currently living in low-lying areas such as Bangladesh and Egypt. In the not-too-distant future, they may be forced to move to higher ground.
- Accelerated coastal erosion has already been blamed for several recent cliff-falls and coastal floods in Britain.
- Changes in the world's vegetation zones will occur as temperatures and patterns of rainfall distribution slowly shift across the planet.
- There could be a 'switch-off' of some ocean currents such as the North Atlantic Drift, which keeps the British Isles relatively mild in winter.
- Malaria, dengue fever and other insect-borne tropical diseases could spread, as global warming creates new areas suitable for the carrier-insects.
- Violent storms, hurricanes and other extreme weather events will become more common.
- There will be an increased risk of prolonged drought in tropical areas and areas that are currently semi-arid, although other areas may experience increased rainfall.
- More frequent and extreme El Niño events in the Pacific are likely. Abnormal temperatures in the surface water of the Pacific Ocean will lead to the failure of the monsoon in South-East Asia and more rain in normally arid areas in South America.

The year 1998 broke many temperature records and was probably the warmest year of the millennium. Sea-levels around the world are known to have risen by an average of 18 cm between 1900 and 2000, and it is predicted that there will be a further rise of at least 24 cm between 2000 and 2050.

It is possible that the effects of global warming may be offset to some extent by increased cloud cover due to more water evaporating from the oceans. Similarly, a greater volume of dust rising from areas suffering drought and desertification will increase the albedo of the upper atmosphere. Widespread plankton growths in the oceans could also remove some of the excess CO_2 from the atmosphere.

Can global warming be stopped?

Many of the initiatives that are being or could be undertaken to reduce acid deposition will also reduce amounts of greenhouse gases. Thus they will also help to control global warming. At the Kyoto and Buenos Aires conferences, the MEDCs pledged that by 2012 they would reduce their CO_2 emissions to 5 per cent below their 1990 levels. This is going to require a much greater dependence on alternative non-polluting sources of energy, such as wind and solar power. Britain is seeking to produce 10 per cent of its electricity from non-fossil fuel sources by 2010. However, there is concern that LEDCs like India and China will actually increase their emissions as poverty is reduced and higher living standards are achieved.

So how can emissions be reduced?

- If the targets for reduced greenhouse gas emissions are to be met, we will have to use cars less and walk, cycle and use public transport more.
- Governments are phasing out the availability of leaded petrol, and tax incentives are designed to encourage the use of smaller, fuel-efficient cars that go further for each litre of fuel.
- The fitting of catalytic converters to all new cars is now compulsory in the EU. These reduce many of the pollutants responsible for urban ozone and acid deposition, but the down-side is that they reduce engine efficiency and use more fuel.
- Much of the energy used to heat our homes and public buildings comes from burning fossil fuels. The amount can be reduced by better insulation, keeping doors and windows closed in winter, stopping draughts and turning the central-heating thermostat down.

Review

10 What is the Earth's **albedo**? In what ways can its effects be upset by air pollution?

11 Write an article for your local newspaper under the headline 'Greenhouse Effect Threatens Our Future'. You should explain its causes to your readers and suggest ways that its impact might be reduced.

12 Outline some possible causes of recent climatic change. In what ways do you think that people may be responsible?

13 Identify some of the likely human consequences of global warming.

14 Carbon dioxide is the most important of the greenhouse gases.
   a Which of the sources shown in **2.9** declined most between 1970 and 1997? What was the reason for this?
   b Which sources do you think should be targeted to make the greatest reductions in output in the future?
   c How might overall reductions be achieved to meet the Kyoto target levels?

Holes in the ozone layer

The **ozone layer** is a band of ozone gas, just a few centimetres thick, that encircles the Earth at a height of about 20 km. It plays a vital role in shielding the planet below from harmful ultraviolet radiation from the Sun. In the 1970s, scientists predicted, and then proved, that each winter the ozone layer over Antarctica was being depleted. In the 1980s evidence from satellite images showed that winter thinning of the ozone layer was also occurring over the Arctic.

The cause of this ozone-thinning appears to be the chlorine present in CFCs. At low temperatures, this acts as a catalyst in a complex series of chemical reactions that effectively destroy the ozone gas in the upper atmosphere. Ozone thinning allows more ultraviolet rays to penetrate this protective shield and to reach the Earth's surface. This can:

- distort plant growth and damage crops
- weaken the human immune system
- cause skin cancers and eye cataracts
- greatly increase the risk of sunburn
- give rise to a range of other health disorders in sunbathers and people working out of doors.

It is important to note that thinning of the ozone layer is **not** a cause of global warming. The ozone layer (when it is thick enough) only absorbs ultraviolet rays from the Sun. The infrared rays responsible for warming the planet's surface are not affected at all by the ozone layer, no matter how thick or thin it is. Confusion sometimes arises because the CFCs that are destroying ozone together form a powerful greenhouse gas.

Enquiry

1   The environmental pressure group Friends of the Earth have drawn up a league table of factories in the UK releasing cancer-causing air pollutants. Called 'Factory Watch', it is available on a website: http://www.foe.co.uk. The industries concerned have described it as 'misleading, alarmist and unnecessary'. What do *you* think?

2   Find out more about the symptoms and causes of bronchitis and asthma.

3   a Where do the highest incidences of respiratory diseases occur in the UK?
   b What environmental factors can you identify that might be responsible for this distribution?
   c Which particular groups in the population are most at risk from these respiratory diseases? What are the reasons for this?

4   Find out more about:
   - current measures being taken to reduce CFC emissions
   - opportunities for the safe disposal of old refrigerators and freezers
   - the precautions people should take to reduce the health risks created by the thinning of the ozone layer.

5   In what ways do too much ozone at low altitudes, but too little ozone in the ozone layer, cause environmental problems?

Water pollution

Human survival depends upon regular supplies of uncontaminated water for drinking and cooking, washing, cleaning, irrigation and a huge variety of industrial processes. Supplies, however, are limited. Whether it comes from underground sources (**aquifers**) or from surface streams, rivers, lakes and reservoirs, water is highly prone to contamination by a wide variety of pollutants. The main sources of freshwater pollution are domestic, industrial and agricultural effluents.

Pollution of the marine environment is also widespread. Although the world's seas and oceans are a vital resource, they are often used as a dump for sewage, industrial effluent and other toxic and radioactive wastes. They are the final depository for pollutants such as nitrates and pesticides washed from the land, either directly through outfall pipes or indirectly via rivers. The sea is also vulnerable to spills associated with the offshore exploitation and transport of oil.

SECTION A

Freshwater pollutants and their sources

Fresh water is a finite resource, yet the demand per head is increasing rapidly in almost every country. In just 30 years, the UK has experienced a 70 per cent increase in domestic water consumption alone. Rivers, lakes and reservoirs are also in huge demand by many recreational pursuits, ranging from angling to sailing. Water quality, however, is under constant threat from pollution from many different sources.

Figure 3.1 Sources of freshwater pollution in England and Wales (1995)

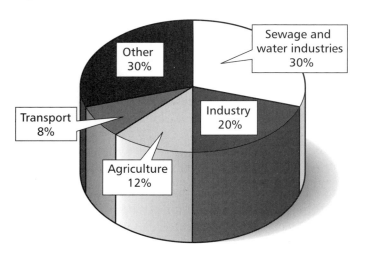

- Other 30%
- Sewage and water industries 30%
- Transport 8%
- Industry 20%
- Agriculture 12%

Water pollution incidents are classified first by the origin or source of the pollutants (**3.1**) and secondly by the type of substances involved (**3.2**). In England and Wales in 1995 there were nearly 26 000 confirmed pollution incidents, although the number of serious incidents (classified by the Environment Agency as 'environmentally damaging') was much lower, 238. The sewage and water supply industry accounted for 30 per cent of all incidents in 1995. Failure of equipment at sewage treatment plants, and overflows during storms and periods of prolonged heavy rainfall, caused most of these.

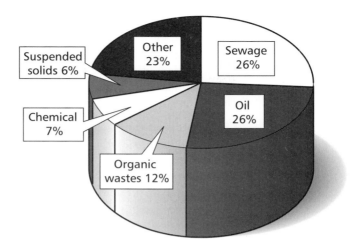

Figure 3.2 Types of freshwater pollutants in England and Wales (1995)

Suspended solids 6%

Other 23%

Sewage 26%

Chemical 7%

Oil 26%

Organic wastes 12%

Sewage pollution contains high levels of nutrients and these encourage the excessive growth of algae in water-courses. This growth turns still or slow-flowing water green, shading out other water plants. If, however, sewage-rich water is able to pass through some kinds of wetland, especially reedbeds, plant stems and roots help to filter the water. They also provide surfaces where bacteria can get to work on the effluent to break it down. Oxygen is essential to this process and it too comes from the reeds. Several water companies are now using reedbeds to treat small quantities of sewage such as the output from a village or a housing estate (**3.3**).

Figure 3.3 The reedbed treatment of sewage

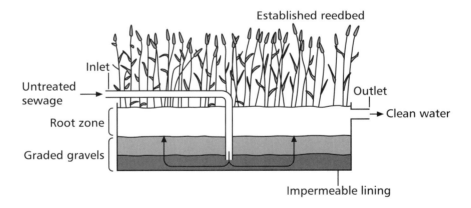

Established reedbed

Inlet

Untreated sewage

Outlet

Clean water

Root zone

Graded gravels

Impermeable lining

Effluent passes right through the reeds' root system to break down the maximum amount of pollutants.

Case study: Water pollution in Delhi

Delhi suffers from some significant water pollution problems. The partially canalised Yamuna River meanders through some 50 km of the city, and for most of this length it is an open sewer. Every day, 1700 million litres of human waste and toxic effluent from industry are poured into the river via 17 major open drains and feeder canals that criss-cross the city. The effluents contaminate wells and water-supply boreholes. Although there are strict pollution control laws in India, their implementation has been far from adequate.

The waters of the Yamuna River are already polluted well before they reach Delhi (see **2.6**). High levels of nitrate fertilisers and other agricultural chemicals, including pesticides such as DDT, come from the area of intensive farmland through which it passes. But the additional pollution as it flows through the city is enormous. Only 2 per cent of the river's total length flows through Delhi, but the city contributes 71 per cent of its heavy pollution load. The water quality of the Yamuna River is so poor that it is incapable of supporting aquatic life-forms such as fish.

This polluted water is known to be the source of many human diseases, both water-borne and carried by insects. These include jaundice, cholera, hepatitis, gastro-enteritis, dysentery, typhoid, malaria (including the more dangerous cerebral malaria) and dengue fever. Figures show that, on average, an Indian child under the age of 5 years will suffer from more than three diarrhoea attacks per year. In 1994, Delhi even experienced an outbreak of plague spread by rats living along polluted water-courses. During each monsoon there is widespread flooding, due to drains choked with rubbish. The spreading waters carry disease still further.

Review

1 Outline the ways in which public water supplies can become polluted.

2 What precautions do you think governments should take to reduce freshwater pollution?

3 What are the problems caused by water pollution in Delhi? In what ways are they different from or similar to those in British cities?

4 How might reedbeds be used in the treatment of polluted water?

SECTION B

Freshwater pollution by industry and transport

Industry

Industry, whether manufacturing or extractive, is a major potential source of water pollution no matter where it is located. Many manufacturing processes produce effluents that are high in pollutants, and their variety is immense. They include harmful organic chemicals (oil and other hydrocarbons) as well as heavy metals, radioactive materials, detergents, nitrates and phosphates.

Quarrying and mining activities are responsible for much water contamination. Gravel washing, erosion of waste-spoil tips and seepage from abandoned mines increase the sediment load of rivers. All over the world, abandoned mines are an ever-present threat to local water-courses. During normal operations both coal and metal-ore mines are continuously drained by large pumps. But when a mine reaches the end of its productive life and is abandoned, the pumps are switched off. Water floods into the disused shafts and tunnels. If iron sulphide minerals are present in the rock, they are oxidised with the help of bacteria present in the water, so forming sulphuric acid. This dissolves any metals exposed in the rock, producing **acid mine deposition** (**AMD**). The solution formed by the process can become highly charged with very toxic metals, such as lead, arsenic and cadmium, which are capable of causing serious chemical pollution.

In Britain alone, it is estimated that at least 580 km of rivers are polluted by AMD as water drains from abandoned mines and spoil heaps. Some of these workings ceased centuries ago. The poisons kill plants, insects, fish and other animals, and can contaminate supplies of drinking water if they percolate through rocks and enter groundwater sources. The problems created for water-courses are demonstrated by the Wheal Jane case study below, but you should also remember that AMD can pollute land (see the Coto Doñana case study in **Chapter 4 Section B**).

Case study: Pollution from Wheal Jane mine (Cornwall)

The problem of flooding and AMD was dramatically demonstrated by the abandoned Wheal Jane tin mine in Cornwall. Wheal Jane was forced to close through economic circumstances in 1991. Pumping ceased and the mine filled with water. The water-table of the adjacent area also rose, filling nearby long-abandoned, and sometimes forgotten, mine tunnels that had, until then, remained dry due to the Wheal Jane pump. Within a radius of 30 km of the site, there are least 30 outflows from other former tin mines, and 240 km of streams and rivers are at risk from pollution. Many of the toxins leaching from the mines are heavy metals and include cadmium, lead, mercury and arsenic.

In January 1992, more than 60 million litres of acidic water stained orange-red with oxidised toxic metals, suddenly burst from a forgotten shaft of a long-abandoned mine. It poured into the beautiful Fal estuary, causing heavy pollution of Carrick Roads (the main entrance to the estuary) and Restronget Creek. Fish, marine mammals and birds were killed. The contamination has had long-lasting effects, because the heavy metals have now entered the food chain and contaminated local shellfish.

To find a solution to the problem of AMD, the Environment Agency has been working with several private firms. Experiments have involved:

- raising the pH of the AMD by adding lime, which causes the dissolved toxic minerals to be precipitated and to settle as a sludge
- using other chemicals that cause dissolved minerals to precipitate, again forming a removable sludge
- encapsulating the toxic metal sludge in a glass-like silica shell that will resist future solution
- developing lagoons with reedbeds that are charged with particular types of bacteria. These treat the AMD by the process of 'sulphate reduction' and effectively reverse the original oxidation process.

None of these methods has yet been perfected or is without some risk to the environment. However, they do seem to have a potential to solve the AMD problem.

Transport

Transport accidents can also cause spillage of pollutants into water-courses. The potential sources of pollution are twofold. First, there is the fuel that is being used by the particular mode of transport: petrol, diesel and other oils. Secondly, there are the substances being transported. Liquids carried by tankers can be particularly toxic and spread rapidly if the containing vessel is ruptured or pierced. It needs to be remembered that many countries still rely on canal and river vessels for the movement of cargo. Spillages and collisions are not unheard of. Any spillages here will be directly into water courses. Remember too that pipelines are another medium used for the movement of liquids and these too are prone to faults.

Review

5 List some of the potential pollutants of water-courses carried by road and rail.

6 Outline the particular water pollution problems that can occur in times of drought and in semi-arid areas.

Case study: Spilt milk

In 1995, 22 000 litres of milk spilled across the road and drained into a tributary of the River Tyne west of Newcastle. This happened when a milk-tanker crashed as a result of a tyre blow-out. Milk is an organic substance that, when broken down by bacteria, is highly polluting. The bacteria removed the oxygen dissolved in the river water, and this killed aquatic invertebrates and fish. Fortunately, much of the potential damage from this incident was avoided, as the spilt milk was quickly pumped onto nearby farmland. But the operation took three days and cost more than £4000 – several times more than the spilt milk was worth!

SECTION C

Freshwater pollution by agriculture

Agriculture produces a great deal of potentially polluting organic waste. It also uses a range of pesticides, artificial fertilisers and even growth hormones which, if allowed to escape into water-courses, can be very damaging to wildlife. Of course, once they have entered streams and rivers, pollutants may be carried as far as the sea. Farming has become more intensive and more specialised in recent years. By using larger amounts of pesticides and artificial fertilisers, more food can be produced from the same area of land. It is because most of these chemicals are soluble that water pollution results.

The major sources of water pollution from agriculture include (**3.4**):

- slurry from cattle and pigs which contains organic waste, ammonia and micro-organisms with traces of antibiotics and growth hormones
- silage effluent, that seeps or overflows from crop storage pits and silos
- dirty water from yard-cleaning and washing root crops
- nitrate and phosphate fertilisers in surface runoff or leached from farmland
- pesticides applied to orchard and field crops and in sheep-dip; also from leaking containers – these can leach through soils to poison both surface and ground waters
- spilt diesel and other fuels
- growth hormones.

Figure 3.4 Potential sources of water pollution on a farm

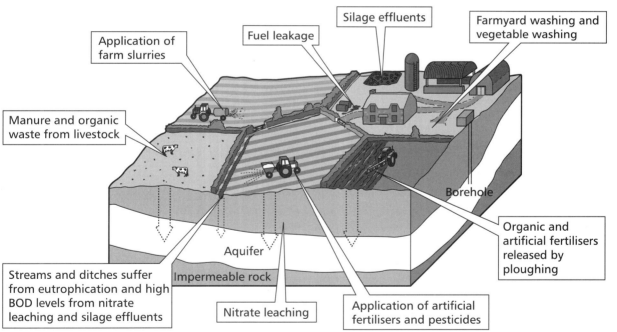

Nitrates are essential for healthy plant growth. They are often applied to arable crops in the form of artificial fertilisers so as to improve yields, but nitrates only become pollutants when they are present in excessive quantities. In some parts of Britain, so much nitrate is leached from farmland that surface waters and drinking water supplies are contaminated. Levels are often above the EU limit of 50 mg per litre.

As a precautionary approach, the Environment Agency has introduced new regulations in Britain to protect particularly sensitive areas under the Nitrate Vulnerable Zones scheme (NVZs) (formerly the Nitrate Sensitive Areas scheme). There are 68 NVZs in Britain where nitrates have reached potentially dangerous levels. Under the scheme, farmers in these zones will be compensated for reducing their nitrate-fertiliser inputs and for implementing a number of other changes to their farming practices. The timing of applications of both artificial fertilisers and organic fertiliser will also be controlled.

Pollution from farm waste such as animal slurries and silage effluents can be a major problem for aquatic life. They contain high levels of organic waste and micro-organisms. Farmers now have to construct waste storage facilities to comply with stringent standards and conform to a Code of Good Practice. Cryptosporidium is an example of a micro-organism found in organic waste. It is a parasite that is difficult both to detect and to remove, and can be the cause of widespread outbreaks of nausea and diarrhoea when it gets into public water supplies.

If the very high organic content of much agricultural waste enters a water-course, bacteria start to break it down. This process uses large amounts of oxygen dissolved in the water, creating a very high **biochemical oxygen demand** (**BOD**). As the demand increases, especially in hot weather, there may not be enough oxygen available in the water for aquatic organisms, such as fish and insects, which then die. This makes the BOD problem even worse as they too decay. The whole ecosystem of the stream or river then collapses, and it can take a long time for it to be fully restored.

Review

7 Identify the different ways in which agriculture can become a water polluter. Try to suggest a ranking of those ways in terms of their seriousness.

8 Explain the significance of **BOD**.

SECTION D

Freshwater pollution by over-pumping

We have seen that water supplies can be polluted if chemicals seep into aquifers from domestic, industrial and agricultural sources. Increasingly, however, there is contamination by salt that seeps into aquifers near the coast, replacing fresh water that is pumped for use. In semi-arid countries and in times of drought, the problem is intensified as the aquifer is over-pumped. The temptation to over-pump and draw in saline water is becoming ever stronger as population increases and demand per head rises.

Case study: Water pollution problems in Israel

With its small territorial extent and arid climate, Israel suffers major problems of inadequate water reserves and a decline in their quality. Most of Israel's water comes from:

- an extensive aquifer (porous rock strata in which water is stored) located near the coast
- an inland aquifer in the mountains (Yarkon-Taninim)
- Lake Kinneret (formerly known as the Sea of Galilee)
- a variety of smaller aquifers.

In each of these water sources, supplies are limited by the low rainfall of the area. There are also problems of pollution from agricultural, industrial and urban sources.

- The **coastal aquifer** suffers particularly from over-extraction. The result is that salt water from the sea has infiltrated the aquifer, and salinity levels are as high as 250 mg per litre. It has also become contaminated by sewage effluent, pesticides and nitrate fertilisers (leached from irrigated areas), by petroleum leaking from old, corroding oil pipelines near Haifa, and spillage at the Ashdod oil refinery.
- The **Yarkon-Taninim aquifer** is now the main source of Israel's drinking water, owing to pollution problems elsewhere. However, the aquifer is limestone. This means that the water is hard, and the highly permeable rock makes the aquifer prone to rapid contamination by pollutants.
- **Lake Kinneret** has experienced eutrophication due to increasing levels of nitrates washed in from its agricultural catchment area. This has altered the balance of the lake's ecosystem, causing algal blooms. These greatly increase the biochemical oxygen demand.

The on-going Israeli–Palestinian conflict and the hostility of neighbouring states, including Syria and Lebanon, have further increased the problems of Israel's limited water supplies, making it virtually impossible to bring water in from elsewhere.

Review

9 What are the consequences of groundwater becoming salinated?

Pollution of seas and oceans

The seas of the world are the final resting place for all the pollution that drains from the land. Much marine pollution is direct, either from the deliberate dumping of waste or by accidental spillage. Many cities around the world empty their raw sewage and industrial effluents straight into the sea with little or no treatment. These effluents contain many of the substances that also cause pollution in fresh water. The list of pollutants is formidable. It includes suspended solids and organic waste, heavy metals, PCBs and other toxins from industry, nitrates and phosphates, pesticides and growth hormones from agriculture. The coastline for many miles around Mumbai (Bombay) is so contaminated with sewage and industrial waste that bathing could be a life-threatening activity. Seafood caught locally is often contaminated with disease organisms and heavy metals. If eaten, these can cause severe stomach upsets and other illness.

Case study: Pollution and coral reefs

Coral reefs are the marine equivalent of tropical rainforests. They have a high biological productivity and a rich biodiversity. Some are a valuable source of local income from tourist activities ranging from skin-diving and reef-viewing through glass-bottomed boats to the sale of coral specimens as souvenirs.

Coral reefs occur in tropical and subtropical seas where the water is shallow, warm and clean. They are excellent indicators of the health of the marine environment. They are also vital spawning areas and nursery grounds for many species of fish, and protect low-lying islands and coasts from erosion. They are important carbon sinks too (see **Chapter 1 Section A**), removing and storing carbon dioxide gas from the atmosphere. Coral polyps live in a close symbiotic relationship with zooxanthellae algae – the corals are nourished by the algae which manufacture food by photosynthesis, while the coral provides shelter, phosphorus and nitrogen for the algae. However, this relationship breaks down if the corals are placed under stress from:

- changes in temperature or salinity
- pollution (especially from land-based sources – fertilisers, sewage effluent and sedimentation resulting from increased deforestation and associated soil erosion)
- increased ultraviolet light
- use of cyanide or dynamite to catch fish around a reef
- over-collection of specimens for souvenirs
- divers treading on them.

Although some scientists suggest it may be a natural cycle, most agree that when placed under stress the coral polyps expel their algae. The reefs become bleached as the corals die. Increased nitrates, phosphates and raw sewage, by causing too much algal growth may also kill the polyps by smothering them. This has happened to corals off Miami in Florida.

In recent years, sea temperatures have risen globally by some 2.4°C, possible evidence of global warming. Increased levels of ultraviolet light have also been received due to thinning of the ozone layer. As a result, many of the world's coral reefs are experiencing severe damage. In the Indian Ocean, 90 per cent of the reefs are now dead, especially those within 150 km of major coastal cities such as Mumbai. Coral reefs in the Red Sea, the Gulf and parts of the Caribbean are showing signs of extreme stress. If present trends continue, 70 per cent of all coral reefs will be destroyed by the year 2030, leading to the deaths of thousands of other species that are dependent on them.

Along many coasts where sea-water has traditionally been clean and unpolluted, conditions are ideal for **aquaculture** – the commercial farming of fish such as salmon and shellfish. The sheltered fjords of Norway, the sea lochs of Scotland's Highlands and Islands and the west coast of Ireland have seen huge increases in this activity in recent years. Today, however, there is increasing concern that these operations are causing pollution. The water becomes over-enriched by nutrients from fish droppings and uneaten food pellets around salmon cages. Pesticides and other chemicals used to control fish lice and disease are concentrated in the area. This pollution is upsetting the balance of the local ecosystem, causing algal blooms and the death of marine invertebrates.

A major cause of marine pollution is the accidental spillage of crude and fuel oil. Supertankers loaded with crude oil pose an obvious threat, and there have been some well-documented incidents in recent years. The *Sea Empress* that went ashore in Pembrokeshire, the *Braer* that foundered on the shore of Shetland and the *Exxon Valdez* that ran aground in Alaska are just a few examples.

Case study: The *Sea Empress* oil spill, Pembrokeshire

The toll of sea life in a major oil spillage can be enormous. The pathetic sight of oiled seabirds struggling ashore provide haunting images of the suffering and damage to wildlife populations that can be inflicted. In 1996, a fully-laden oil tanker, the *Sea Empress*, ran aground on the Pembrokeshire coast, close to the entrance to Milford Haven harbour in south-west Wales.

The *Sea Empress* accident resulted in:

- 72 000 tonnes of oil spilled
- 200 km of coastline polluted
- 7000 seabirds oiled
- seals and other marine life killed
- serious damage to tourism and the inshore fishing industry in the area
- £60 million spent on cleaning up the beaches
- a £5 million fine for the Milford Haven port authorities – in the official enquiry, poor piloting of the tanker was blamed for the accident.

The oil companies claim that seabirds and other marine animals are appealing creatures, and the emotive pictures of the oiled victims shown on TV leave the public with the impression that the impact of an oilspill is far worse than it really is. However, cleaning up after a spillage can cause more subtle damage to the local marine ecosystem, and prolong its recovery time. The detergents used to disperse the oil kill algae, plankton, molluscs and fish, removing many links in the food chain on which larger fish, marine mammals and birds depend. Although detergents may sink the oil so that it is no longer a surface hazard, scientific research has found that it makes the oil on the seabed more persistent.

Major spillage incidents hit the headlines, but every day smaller quantities of spilled oil also take their toll. This might be from the illegal flushing of fuel-oil tanks at sea. Minor accidental spillage, leakage by shipping and offshore natural gas and oil extraction operations, such as those in the North Sea, are other possibilities. In 1997, oil spillage incidents around the coastline of Britain increased by 7 per cent. This was the third year running in which a rise had been recorded. Some of the most affected waters are the Straits of Dover, the Thames and Humber estuaries, the firths of the Clyde, the Solway, the Forth and the Moray, as well as Shetland's inshore waters.

Review

10 In what ways are the causes of freshwater pollution **a** similar to, and **b** different from pollution of the sea?

11 Why is aquaculture a source of marine pollution?

Enquiry

1   What are the criteria for designating an area as a **nitrate vulnerable zone**? What measures does the scheme take to ensure that nitrate inputs are reduced in such areas?

2   In Europe, the Blue Flag Beach award has been introduced. It sets a standard by which the safety of sea water for bathing can be assessed. Find out more about the criteria that are tested before a place is granted Blue Flag status for beach cleanliness.

3   What measures have been taken and applied internationally to reduce the risk of oil spillages at sea?

4

Land pollution

Most chemical pollutants only become a problem to land and soil when they are soluble in water. Rain and melting snow leaches dissolved pollutants into streams and aquifers. Thus the problems of land, air and water pollution are closely interlinked. Land pollution can be caused by waste disposal, mining and quarrying, industrial decline and dereliction, and industrial accidents. There is also considerable land pollution from agricultural sources such as fertilisers, pesticides, slurry and other organic wastes.

In small countries such as the UK, land is in short supply. Careful decisions must be made about its sustainable use. This raises the question of where new housing should be built to meet the escalating demand. Should the 'urban exodus' be further encouraged by releasing more 'green' countryside for development, resulting in urban sprawl? Or should abandoned industrial and other derelict sites (**brownfield sites**) be redeveloped instead, bearing in mind the high clean-up costs involved if the land has been contaminated?

SECTION A

By waste disposal

Waste is material that no longer serves any useful purpose, and so we throw it away. In England and Wales alone, each person produces about a third of a tonne of rubbish each year. Over 122 million tonnes of waste from domestic and industrial sources has to be disposed of annually (**4.1**). This amount of rubbish is a reflection of how many resources we consume. We live in a high-consumption/throw-away society. So long as the dustmen collect and empty the dustbin each week, we tend to forget about the environment and the problems that disposing of our rubbish can cause.

Figure 4.1 The typical composition of household refuse in the UK

	% of total weight
Paper and card	33
Organic matter	21
Debris, dust and cinders	17
Plastics	11
Glass	9
Metals	7
Textiles	2

All waste is potentially an environmental hazard. It ranges from unsightly litter in the street or on the beach to chemical contamination of soil, air and water. Waste, whether from domestic or industrial sources, must be disposed of safely, with the least impact on the environment, and at the lowest cost. Burial in holes in the ground is by far the most common method. About 90 per cent of domestic waste is disposed of in this way. However, sites used for **landfill** must be carefully chosen as they can easily become unsightly, smelly, a source of windblown litter, flies and vermin. Some domestic waste contains poisonous substances – for example mercury and cadmium in dead batteries, garden chemicals and unwanted medicines.

The problem with landfill is that it makes little practical use of the waste material (**4.2**). It also takes up valuable land space until such time as the site is full and can be redeveloped. Even then, careful consideration must be given to the site's after-use. A former rubbish tip may not be an ideal site for new housing, for example. Landfill also depends on a suitable hole in the ground being available – perhaps a former quarry, gravel or clay pit. The UK Government has imposed a landfill tax – currently £10 per tonne for potentially polluting wastes, and £2 per tonne for inert materials – to encourage industry to reduce waste and to look at the whole life-cycle of their products.

Figure 4.2 A bulldozer at work on a huge rubbish tip

Case study: Walkers Snack Foods and waste reduction

The Walkers Snack Foods Company, based at Peterlee in north-east England, recently reviewed its whole manufacturing strategy, with 'waste minimisation' as its main objective. In consultation with employees, a new strategy was drawn up. Staff were trained and, because they had been involved in the planning, were highly motivated to implement the scheme and make it a success. Targets were set and monitored, and waste segregated into different types that could be sold to various recycling companies in the area.

In the first year alone, the company saved nearly £1 million by recycling the waste it produced. As less waste now goes to landfill there are substantial savings made on the landfill taxes that would otherwise have been paid. Water consumption has been reduced by 19%, the biochemical oxygen demand (BOD) of effluents has decreased significantly, and carbon dioxide emissions have been cut by 1200 tonnes a year (6%).

If rubbish is not disposed of as landfill, then it must be burnt. But the fumes released from the incinerators can contain hydrochloric acid (from burning plastics), dioxins and heavy metals, thus adding to air pollution. In the UK, local authorities operate only 30 domestic waste incinerators, and EU laws strictly regulate the way they function. On the plus side, some European cities use the heat produced by domestic waste incinerators to generate electricity and for central heating of nearby hospitals, houses and flats. In Switzerland, 80 per cent of combustible domestic waste is disposed of in this way.

Organic waste decays when it is dumped in landfill sites. Carbon dioxide and methane – both greenhouse gases – are given off. Molecule for molecule, methane is much more potent as a greenhouse gas than carbon dioxide. Methane is also potentially explosive and can cause a fire if it collects in an enclosed place such as a building.

At Chichester, Sussex, several large disused gravel pits have been filled with rubbish and, like most domestic waste, it has a high organic content. Some of the methane gas produced is burnt off at flare pipes, but in places special vent pipes with rotating cowls have been inserted deep into the waste to disperse the gas. In Bedfordshire, a more positive solution to the problem has been adopted. Former clay pits, dug for brick-making, have been filled with household rubbish and capped with impervious clay, and the methane gas is now collected. It is used as biogas for firing brick-kilns and as a fuel source for a small electric power station.

Another option for disposal of organic waste is to convert it to compost. This can give several environmental benefits. It reduces emissions, and the compost produced improves the organic content of soil. Compost is a substitute for peat dug from lowland raised-bogs, thus helping to save a threatened wildlife habitat. There are many examples of composting schemes around the world. The use of worms to make compost (**vermiculture**) from biodegradable organic rubbish obtained from large urban areas is increasingly practised in warmer climates.

Figure 4.3 A compost-making plant, Pune

Much of the organic rubbish thrown out by people living in and around the city of Pune (India) is now converted to compost. This rubbish is pre-sorted and the biodegradable material collected and transported to a vermiculture compost-making unit located in an agricultural area some 25 km away.

The organic waste is spread in rows, watered to ensure the correct humidity and 'seeded' with brandling worms imported from Europe (apparently they are more efficient than local worms). The material decays quickly as the worms get to work in the high temperatures, and in a few days it has been converted into a nutrient-rich compost. Local farmers purchase the product at very low cost and benefit from the greatly improved crop yields that the compost gives. They are spared the expense of using costly artificial fertilisers. This has proved to be cost-effective, and the technique is now being adopted by other Indian cities, notably in Bangalore.

In Germany and Switzerland, domestic waste is segregated by householders into different-coloured bags or bins before collection for disposal. The different categories can then be recycled, and the organic waste composted. As much as 85 per cent of Switzerland's trash glass is now recycled. Figure 4.4 gives some indication that we all have a long way to go before we can claim to be *thoroughly* recycling household waste.

Figure 4.4 Potential for recycling household waste if it is pre-sorted

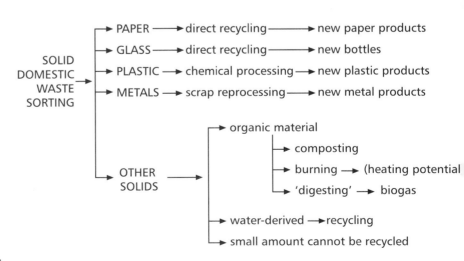

By extractive industries

To prevent any repetition of such tragic accidents as the Aberfan spoil-heap disaster of 1966, tips of waste rock and spoil from mines and quarries need to be stabilised. It would seem to be a good idea, therefore, to plant them up so that roots can bind loose material, while leaves and stems protect the surface from rain-splash and hail. However, it is often very difficult to get plant cover to grow on areas left derelict by mining activities. This may be due to poisons such as lead, mercury, nickel, cadmium and copper contained in the waste material. These elements are toxic to plants, fungi and bacteria.

Spoil-tips can:

- suffer erosion due to their steep sides
- contain toxic metals and other poisons which make them unsuitable for plants
- catch fire spontaneously (most common in colliery spoil-tips)
- lack key plant nutrients
- be made of coarse materials, and therefore are too freely drained and unstable for plant growth
- be made of too many fine clay particles, which cause water-logging.

Abandoned coal mines, and mines from which metal ores have been extracted, can be a major source of pollution. In **Chapter 3** we saw how acid mine deposition (AMD) flooding from the worked-out Wheal Jane tin mine in Cornwall contaminated the Fal estuary. Land bordering canals, streams and rivers polluted by AMD can also be contaminated by the toxic chemicals seeping into the soil, or deposited on the surface by a flood. This can destroy crops, livestock and wildlife, and make the area unusable for many years.

Case study: Toxic spill near Coto Doñana National Park, Spain

The Coto Doñana National Park is an area of some 77 260 ha that lies to the south of Seville in Spain (**4.5**). It is the delta of the Guadiamar and

Guadalquivir rivers, a mosaic of marshland, forest and sand dunes, noted for its outstanding wildlife. It is home to rare birds, mammals, reptiles, insects and plants. The Park is threatened by a number of problems including:

- contamination by pesticides from surrounding agricultural land
- urban development at nearby beach resorts
- a falling water-table due to over-pumping
- competition between indigenous species and introduced species.

Figure 4.5 Coto Doñana National Park

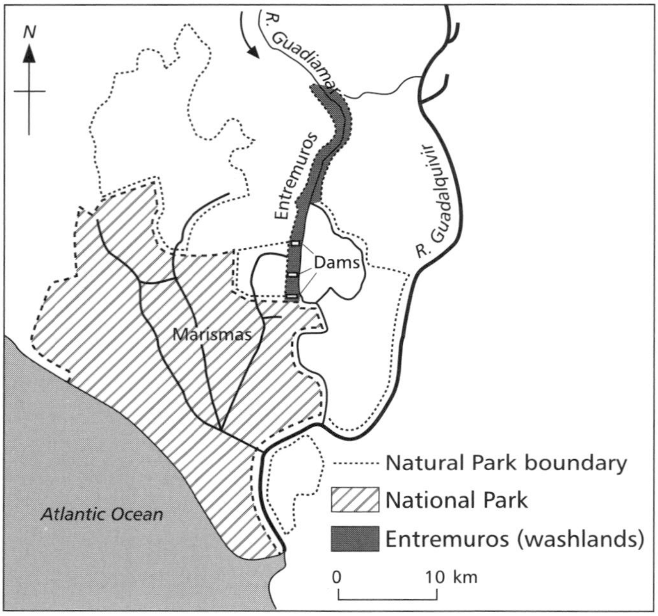

Natural Park boundary
National Park
Entremuros (washlands)

0   10 km

The vulnerability of the Park to another threat was underlined on 24 April 1998. This was the day that a dam holding back toxic waste from zinc, lead, copper and silver mining activities, burst. The Los Frailes zinc mine is some 60 km from Coto Doñana, but a 50 metre wide breach in the dam sent a wall of water contaminated by AMD down the Guadiamar River. For five days, 7 million tonnes of toxic mud spread along the river's course. Toxic sludge covered 4700 ha of rice fields, 4400 ha of grazing, arable and woodland and 800 ha of marsh. The acid waters then entered the *entremuros*, a series of washlands between retaining banks and dams – an important breeding area for wetland birds.

Nearly 10 000 ha of farm and woodland alongside the river have been seriously damaged by the spill. Much of the sludge, which contains arsenic and cadmium, has since been mechanically removed, but during the flood that followed, the toxins penetrated at least 20 cm into the soil. Citizens of seven towns have been warned not to drink the local water for the foreseeable future, not even from the deepest wells. Farmers have been forced to remove their sheep and cattle from the area, rice and vegetable growing is impossible, and commercial fishing has been seriously affected (26 tonnes of dead fish were found).

Some conservation organisations, including the WorldWide Fund for Nature (Spain) have criticised the Spanish authorities for being too complacent and trying to hush-up the entire episode. They believe the army should be called in to safeguard the area, to help remove contaminated soil, and to enforce more adequate surveillance mechanisms. They call for the Los Frailes mine to be shut down and for the employees of the mining company to be provided with alternative work.

Review

3 a In what ways are disused mines and spoil tips a hazard to the local environment?

b How might those hazards you have identified be reduced?

By agriculture

Even in highly urbanised countries like the UK, something close to 80 per cent of the land area is used by agriculture. So it is important that care for the environment is combined at every point with efficient farming operations. This means controlling pollution and avoiding soil damage whenever possible. It also means that farmers as 'custodians of the countryside' have a responsibility to conserve and enhance landscapes and wildlife habitats.

As with water (**Chapter 3 Section C**), agricultural sources of land pollution include the application of manures, artificial fertilisers and pesticides, and the disposal of slurries. These may be both solids and liquids. Liquids need to be applied by spraying, and this can cause problems if strong winds cause the spray to drift into hedges and water-courses. The application of insecticides by low-flying aircraft can accidentally cause spray-drift and unwanted contamination. Mercifully, due to its cost and the risk to local residents and wildlife, this method of application is now much reduced in the UK. When solid fertilisers are applied, direct drilling into the soil rather than scattering it over the surface prevents non-target areas from damage.

Pests and diseases take a heavy toll of agricultural production, and many farmers maintain control by using a wide range of pesticides. Unfortunately, pesticides can be washed off the crops and leach through soils into groundwater and surface channels, contaminating adjacent wetlands, streams, rivers, hedgerows and woodlands. Much research has been carried out to improve safety standards in the industry, and codes of practice and legislation have been introduced. These aim to reduce the risk of harm to farm-workers, consumers of the produce and non-target species of wildlife. The use of persistent organo-chlorine insecticides such as Dieldrin and DDT, which had such devastating effects on wildlife in the UK during the 1950s and '60s, has ceased. However, they are still being used in some LEDCs and imported foodstuffs have to be regularly monitored for residues.

Some beneficial species have been harmed by the too frequent use of non-specific insecticides. These include ladybirds (which eat huge quantities of aphids), beetles and spiders. The result has been that the aphid pests, which the chemicals were trying to control, are more likely to flourish, as they now have fewer natural predators. Increasingly, pesticides are being created that are specific to particular pests. Biological pest control is also being encouraged as an alternative to the use of damaging chemicals, especially in commercial glasshouse crop and horticultural production. This technique involves the release of insects and fungi that are parasitic on the pest species. There are possibilities for extending this approach into field crops.

Increased organic farming could provide part of the answer for a more sustainable and environmentally friendly agriculture. MAFF has several incentive schemes to promote it. Organic farming bans the use of pesticides and artificial fertilisers, but encourages biological methods of pest control, while organic fertilisers and crop rotations are used to maintain fertility. Organically-grown produce commands higher prices in the supermarkets, and demand appears to be increasing. This is particularly so in an age of growing concern about genetic engineering and the genetic modification of food crops (see **Chapter 8 Section D**). Advocates of organic farming also point out that its methods improve soil quality and produce more healthy and better flavoured food.

In hot, arid areas, it is often necessary to irrigate land in order to grow crops. However, this can be the cause of soil pollution by **salinisation**. This occurs particularly in coastal areas when sea water seeps into pervious rocks. Elsewhere it occurs when salts in solution are drawn up from groundwater to the surface and are then concentrated by evaporation. In many irrigation projects in tropical and subtropical areas more than 25 per cent of the irrigated area can be affected by salinisation (see **Chapter 3 Section C**).

Soils in areas of high rainfall may also be rendered unusable if vegetation is cleared for farming, and soils are exposed to the full effects of the climate. This is especially the case in the rainforests where laterisation is a major problem for tropical soils. With forest clearance, the latosol soils are exposed to heavy rain and hot sun. Aluminium and iron oxides in the soil are drawn to the surface by evaporation. These upward movements of water and dissolved minerals are called **translocations**. The minerals are baked by the hot sun and a hard impervious laterite crust forms on the surface. This prevents plant growth and encourages gullying and soil erosion.

Review

4 What are pesticides, and what problems are associated with their use?

5 How can soils be better protected from damage in **a** hot, arid climates and **b** tropical rainforests?

Brownfield versus greenfield

With rising populations and changing patterns of living, land for housing is in short supply in many parts of the world. In the UK, rural areas, especially those designated as **green belts**, are facing increasing pressure for land to be released for the building of new homes. Objectors point out that housing developments in more rural areas increase energy demands, and therefore air pollution, because people living there need to commute to towns and cities for work and services.

Ironically, following severe industrial decline, there are thousands of hectares of derelict land in many parts of Europe and the United States

Figure 4.6 The Millennium Dome at Greenwich – built on a typical brownfield site

(**4.6**). Most land of this kind, also called **brownfield** land, has a long industrial history. Much is located in the industrial conurbations that developed on the coalfields following the Industrial Revolution. The potential for redeveloping such land for housing and new industries raises many issues. The location of the Millennium Dome in Greenwich is a brownfield site and there are examples of the use of such sites for garden festivals in Liverpool, Stoke, Ebbw Vale and Glasgow.

Although Britain's population growth is almost static, there is an increasing demand for additional housing. This is due to:

- the decline of the nuclear family and increasing numbers of single people, divorcees and single-parent families requiring housing
- continuing migration towards the southern half of the country
- the 'urban exodus' – the demand for home ownership in peaceful rural surroundings away from city centres.

Originally it had been proposed that 60–75 per cent of the 4.4 million new homes required in the UK could be accommodated in brownfield locations, but it has become increasingly apparent that such targets are unrealistic, at least in the South. The Government has now reduced its target to 50 per cent on brownfield sites.

Unfortunately for the Government, the greatest demand for new housing is focused on the southern counties from Cornwall to Norfolk. These are the areas with the fewest brownfield locations. This means that land in the protected green belts adjacent to existing towns and their suburban areas will need to be released. In other words, planning regulations will need to be relaxed and development permitted on agricultural land or **greenfield** sites.

The issue is further complicated by the fact that brownfield sites are often contaminated by various pollutants, including acid deposition, toxic heavy metals, dioxins, and other chemicals. Many are too noisy, close to main roads and railways, and people do not wish to live in such places. A huge investment is required to clean them up before redevelopment can take place. The question arises as to 'Who should pay?'

Case study: Countryside under development pressure in Cambridgeshire

Rural Cambridgeshire is facing the daunting prospect of having to accommodate nearly 210 000 new homes between the years 2000 and 2016. The demand is created by the huge growth in the new high-technology industries attracted by the proximity of Cambridge University. There is widespread public concern about the proposal, and people are particularly anxious to protect rural land around the ancient university city. The proposals are that six new towns with populations between 10 000 and 50 000 should be constructed. Three of them could be established on sites that are currently used as military bases and airfields, but the rest would need to be on greenfield sites.

Case study: Brownfield development in Hampshire?

Hampshire needs between 40 000 and 60 000 new homes, to be built between 2001 and 2011. At present there is a conflict between the Hampshire County Council and the Portsmouth and Southampton local authorities. Hampshire County Council proposes that the new homes should be built within the existing urban areas, mainly in Portsmouth and Southampton, but also in Andover, Winchester, Basingstoke and Micheldever. It suggests that much of the expansion could be achieved by urban renewal. However, Portsmouth and Southampton would prefer to see the development taking place on greenfield sites outside their areas. Part of their reluctance to redevelop brownfield locations is the potentially high clean-up costs for clearing environmental contamination before any building could proceed.

Review

6 What do you understand by the term **brownfield site**?

7 Argue the cases for and against the development of brownfield and greenfield sites to solve Britain's future housing problems. Do you think the government should subsidise development on brownfield sites to protect the countryside?

1   Many farmers are proud of their role as 'custodians of the countryside'. What do you think of the notion that farmers should be compensated for theoretical loss of production by safeguarding wildlife and landscape quality?

2   Find out more about the Environmentally Friendly Farming Schemes available to farmers through MAFF (Ministry of Agriculture, Fisheries and Food). The latest information is available by searching the MAFF website. Other information on environmental matters may be found on the Internet from the DoET (Department of Environment and Transport) website and the Open Government website:

    http://www.open.gov.uk/index.htm

3   There is a view that since farmers receive subsidies and incentives for good environmental practice, the general public should be allowed greater access to farmland for recreational purposes. This is sometimes called 'The right to roam'. What are your views on this issue? What would the implications be for **a** agriculture and **b** the environment, if more public access were to be allowed?

5

Aesthetic pollution

The eye of the beholder

Aesthetic pollution is a potentially more controversial topic than pollution by chemicals. This is because most judgements about it are almost inevitably of a highly subjective nature. It includes three different forms, each to do with one of the senses:

- **noise pollution**
- **visual pollution**
- **olfactory pollution** – foul-smelling fumes from a factory, the smell of a sewage treatment works or of slurry being spread on farmland.

In recent years, arguments relating to aesthetic pollution have been put forward in debates about development proposals. Most often, of course, the possibility of aesthetic pollution is put forward to support actions aimed at protection and conservation.

It is much more difficult to be objective about aesthetic pollution than other adverse influences on environmental quality. The perception of the aesthetic qualities of a place – the features thought to contribute to its character – is a truly individual or personal matter. Things that delight one person may appal another. Some people delight in the sound of children playing, while others regard it as an intrusive nuisance. This point is exemplified by a recent proposal to limit the numbers of motor-powered boats using Lake Windermere in the Lake District. One reason given for limiting numbers was safety, given the severe overcrowding of the water at peak holiday times. Noise pollution also came into the equation. Many people visiting the area derive enormous pleasure from seeing boats speeding across the surface of the lake. Other visitors, however, go there to enjoy the beautiful scenery, and its traditional peace and quiet. For them, the noise of the boats has become so excessive that it ruins their pleasure of a visit to Windermere.

Review

1 Write your own definition of **aesthetic pollution**.

2 Suggest a possible classification of aesthetic pollutants.

3 Can you think of some environmental issues that have an important aesthetic dimension?

Noise pollution

Noise pollution can be defined as any unwanted sound. Exposure to noise in the environment affects the quality of many people's lives. Sounds range from those that are simply annoying, such as rustling crisp packets and loud whispers in a cinema, perhaps, or aircraft noise that disrupts lessons in school, to noise levels that are so great they can cause hearing loss, hypertension and even heart attacks.

The intensity or loudness of noise is measured in **decibels** (**dB**). The World Health Organisation considers that daytime noise levels exceeding 55 dB are unacceptable, and if levels are above this they begin to constitute a health hazard. Sources of noise pollution are just as varied as for other forms of pollution. Road vehicles, railways, aircraft, industry, construction and recreation are among the major producers. But army firing ranges and quarries are significant noise polluters too. In towns and cities with high population densities and cramped living conditions, 'noisy neighbours' can produce high decibel levels. Sources of disturbing noise range from burglar and car alarms to noisy crowds at sporting events, riotous parties and excessively amplified music.

The European Environment Agency reports that 113 million Europeans are regularly subjected to more than 65 dB from the sources outlined above. In the Netherlands alone, more than 1 million people are subjected to excessive noise because they live beneath the flight-path of Schiphol Airport. Similar problems occur for people living close to London's Heathrow Airport. In the period 1988–98, the annual number of passengers using Heathrow increased from 31 million to more than 57 million. Flights in and out of Heathrow have risen from 282 000 to 423 000 a year – an increase of some 50 per cent. Night flying from Heathrow is banned so that the noise of flight operations is largely concentrated between 07.00 and 23.00 hours.

Case study: Manchester airport's second runway

When completed, the second runway at ManchesterAirport will enable it to handle 30 million passengers per year, overtaking London's Gatwick Airport to become Britain's second busiest airfield. Construction work began in 1997 but the proposal was the subject of a long and heated controversy.

Although the scheme will attract 50 000 new jobs to the area, it was strongly opposed by local residents and 'green' lobbyists. Protestors built a network of tunnels in the ground and tree-houses and rope-walkways in woodland on the site, and succeeded in delaying work there for several weeks. Their objections focused on the demolition of several historic houses dating from 1602, and the need to clear areas of woodland and countryside that are home to some important wildlife species. Another point of objection was the greatly increased level of noise pollution that can be anticipated from more traffic and aircraft movements. Protestors claim that the costs of the new runway can only be justified if it is operated at night as well as during the day.

Figure 5.1 Aircraft flying low over housing near Heathrow Airport

Northolt Airport as an overflow for Heathrow

London's Heathrow Airport is already operating at peak capacity. In order to ease the pressure, it is proposed that the nearby Northolt Airport at Hillingdon should be greatly expanded and used as an overflow. Early in 1999, Northolt had just 18 RAF military and VIP flights (including the Royal Family) per day, with a maximum of 7000 take-offs and landings in a year. As the runway is too short to handle large aircraft, the proposal is that smaller planes of up to 100 seats and mainly used on domestic flights, should be transferred to Northolt. This would increase take-offs and landings to 12 per hour or 35 000 a year – a five-fold increase.

There is strong local opposition to the proposal. Objectors claim the following:

- There will be a great increase in noise pollution affecting a radius of at least 1 km around the airport itself. The noise will come from both ground movements of aircraft and aircraft using the flight paths. Large residential areas directly beneath the flight paths include Uxbridge, Ruislip, Eastcote and North Hillingdon.
- There will be a huge increase in road traffic. Local roads are already very congested and any increase will also add to problems of noise pollution.
- The increased number of aircraft and additional motor traffic will both increase air pollution from exhaust fumes.
- Much of the land immediately adjacent to Northolt is in the green belt. As the necessary infrastructure of new terminal building, car and coach parks, hotels and airline offices cannot be accommodated on the existing site alone, they will have to eat into the green belt.
- Construction work will create noise disturbance, dust and lorry traffic.

According to a survey by the Building Research Establishment, road traffic is the most common noise disturbing people in the UK. Sound from busy roads can carry for a distance of up to 5 km; 70 per cent of people object to it and 80 per cent say they are irritated by it. While the amount of sound is dependent on the type of road surface, tyre noise produced by cars travelling at more than 50 km/h is responsible for most of the noise pollution. Attempts are often made to plant up the margins of motorways and busy trunk roads with shrubs and trees to muffle the sound. Sections of the M25 passing through residential areas in Surrey have also been edged with tall fences to provide a sound baffle.

The Countryside Commission looks at sound pollution in another way. They have attempted to identify **tranquil areas**. These are defined as 'places considered unspoilt by visual and sound pollution'. A place qualifies as a tranquil area if it is:

- 4 km from a large power station
- 3 km from a road with dense traffic
- 2 km from most other motorways and trunk roads
- 1 km from a road causing medium disturbance
- away from zones of noise coming from airport flight paths, railway lines and intensive open-cast mining
- not within sight of overhead powerlines.

Using these criteria, only 56 per cent of England could be classed as 'tranquil' in 1999, and this area is shrinking rapidly.

Case study: Noise pollution in Delhi

As if Delhi's air and water pollution problems were not enough, noise pollution is another 'public enemy', and it is increasing rapidly. Warnings by the World Health Organisation that daily exposure to sound levels of more than 55 dB can cause health problems (including hypertension, headaches, sleep loss, fatigue and a lack of concentration) are met with a cynical laugh by the residents of Delhi. The average person here is continually exposed to a cacophony of deafening noises – vehicle horns, engine roar from lorries, buses and cars, high-pitched sirens and aircraft noise. Delhi's Indira Gandhi International Airport has its highest levels of international flight traffic arriving and departing between midnight and dawn. There is also excessive noise of loud music from radios and loudspeaker systems. Noise levels in Delhi regularly exceed 100 dB and the city now ranks as one of the world's noisiest.

Although noise was recognised as a pollutant in the 1986 Environmental Protection Act, so far there are few laws designed to restrict noise levels. Only Delhi's traffic police have the right to book drivers for creating undue noise and for playing excessively loud music while driving.

Case study: High-speed rail-link between London and the Channel Tunnel

Speed, convenience and comfort were the key words of those who planned the Channel Tunnel joining England and France. A high-speed rail-link providing rapid city-centre to city-centre travel between London, Paris and Brussels was always an integral part of the Channel Tunnel project. In France the high-speed track was available from the time of the Tunnel's opening; trains here travel at a top speed of 300 km/h. The Belgian high-speed link was opened in 1997. However, the English link from Folkestone into London will not be available until 2004 at the earliest. Currently, the Eurostar trains travel on some 100 km of old track reaching a maximum speed of 160 km/h, but slower than this for much of the journey, to reach the present terminus at Waterloo. When the high-speed link is completed to the planned terminal at St Pancras International, the journey time will be reduced by 30 minutes.

Figure 5.2 The high-speed rail link between London and the Channel Tunnel

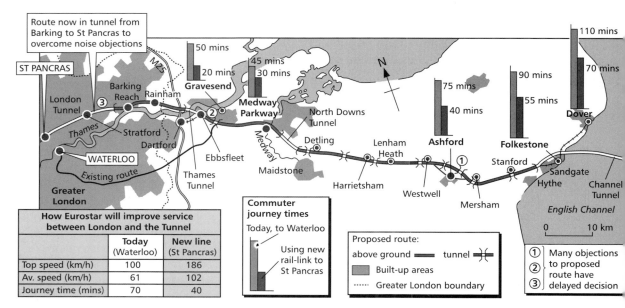

How Eurostar will improve service between London and the Tunnel

	Today (Waterloo)	New line (St Pancras)
Top speed (km/h)	100	186
Av. speed (km/h)	61	102
Journey time (mins)	70	40

Commuter journey times
Today, to Waterloo
Using new rail-link to St Pancras

Proposed route:
above ground ▬▬ tunnel ⊁⊬
 ▨ Built-up areas
······ Greater London boundary

① Many objections to proposed route have delayed decision
②
③

While lack of finance has been one reason for the delay, there has also been a failure by the Government and planners to agree on the route that the line will follow (**5.2**). The proposed route has been subject to almost constant readjustment as a result of vigorous opposition by different groups of local objectors along the proposed route, on the grounds of noise pollution and disturbance. This has become a classic example of **NIMBYism** (NIMBY = Not In My Back Yard). The irony is that many of the link's potential customers live near to the ideal route and some are the very people who complain at the lengthy delays in completing the link on the English side of the Tunnel.

To meet many of the local objections, much of the route through built-up areas will now be underground, the cost of tunnelling greatly adding to the cost and construction time of the scheme.

SECTION C

Visual pollution

As indicated in the introduction to this chapter, 'Beauty is in the eye of the beholder'. While the concept of visual pollution of our fragile environment is more controversial than other forms of pollution, it is nevertheless an important one. A place can be said to be suffering from visual pollution if there is too much litter lying about, or there is graffiti on walls and buildings. Other eyesores include unkempt gardens, poorly maintained buildings, a profusion of advertising hoardings in inappropriate places, intrusive coloured paintwork, inappropriate location of factories and tall chimneys, aerials and radio-masts, overhead powerlines, buildings that are misfits with other buildings in an area – the list is seemingly endless (**5.3**).

Figure 5.3 Examples of visual pollution

Perhaps one of the easier visual pollution problems to deal with is litter. There are many educational campaigns led by such organisations as the Tidy Britain Group, which implore people to 'Take Your Rubbish Home' or 'Bag It and Bin It'. We can all take greater personal responsibility for litter, but a major source, especially in urban areas, is illegal fly-tipping. Heavier fines and stronger enforcement of the laws against casual waste dumping may be necessary.

The mobile phone companies have been severely criticised for their visually intrusive telecommunications masts that are scattered at regular intervals across the British landscape. One company (Vodaphone) is now attempting to camouflage its masts and aerials by disguising them as trees made from plastic. Others are being hidden behind false plastic walls on buildings using special techniques drawn from the film industry in building film sets.

Visual pollution is often linked with a variety of other environmental threats. An excellent example is provided by attempts to produce a greater proportion of our electricity from renewable, non-polluting (in the chemical sense) sources such as wind power, outlined in the case study below. While development of wind power will reduce the overall demand for electricity produced by fossil fuels, wind farm developments themselves are often opposed on grounds of both visual and noise pollution.

Case study: Wind farms in the UK

At the International Conferences on Climatic Change in Kyoto (1997) and Buenos Aires (1998), the UK signed-up to a number of international agreements and set targets to reduce its emissions of carbon dioxide and other greenhouse gases. One way of doing so will be to produce more electricity from renewable resources. Indeed, the UK has set a target that by 2100, 10 per cent of Britain's energy will come from renewable resources. Wind power is one of the most obvious of these.

In recent years, there have been major advances in wind turbine technology, so that the unit cost of production has been greatly reduced. In 1990, wind-generated electricity cost about 9p per kilowatt-hour – considerably more expensive than power produced by traditional power stations burning fossil and nuclear fuels. By 1999, new 1.5 megawatt wind turbines, with a power output 150 per cent greater than those available in 1990, had reduced production costs to less than 3p per kilowatt hour for land-based wind farms, and 5.5p for those constructed out at sea.

Unfortunately, the new turbine-towers are taller than the older units (71 metres compared with 49 metres), making them even more obvious in

Figure 5.4 Wind farms are sometimes built in scenically attractive areas

the landscape. Increasingly, planning permission for new wind farms is being refused on the grounds that they are visual blots on the landscape. Between 1994 and 1999, only two of eighteen planning permission requests were approved. One such example was the refusal late in 1998 to allow the development of a wind farm consisting of 25 of the new turbines at Barningham High Moor in County Durham. Some interesting arguments were put forward by the planning authorities to justify their refusal. Not only would the development be unacceptable visually, they also pointed out that wind power development would only make a small contribution to Britain's total energy needs. When viewed against the likely huge increases in greenhouse gas emissions from such countries as India and China as they develop, the savings made by developing wind power in the UK would be so minuscule as to be irrelevant.

Nevertheless, the Government says it regards the development of wind power as a continuing priority, and points to recent surveys of public opinion in Cornwall and Powys, Britain's main areas of wind power development. In both areas there is a large majority of the local population in favour. In order to meet some of the more general opposition, it is expected that more wind power developments will take place offshore, well away from sensitive areas of outstanding natural beauty. But even these sites are not without their objectors, who claim they will disturb birds and other marine life.

Sometimes long-established quarries and manufacturing industries are found within areas that have since been designated a National Park or AONB. Quarries have been landscape features for centuries and the minerals extracted are crucial to the national economy. In such areas, special attention is given to landscape restoration and impact of the operation. Nevertheless, there are many examples of visual pollution in protected areas, as can be seen from the case study on the next page.

Case study: Hope Valley cement works

The Hope Valley cement works is a controversial development located near Castleton in the core of the Peak District National Park in Derbyshire. Its chimney and processing plant can be seen from a long way away, especially from the surrounding hills. Large amounts of limestone are quarried from within the Park, but coal to fuel the process must be transported from outside.

Apart from its visual impact on the landscape, the works produces fumes, noise, dust and traffic too. However, as it manufactures nearly 10 per cent of Britain's cement requirements, and has long-term planning permission to extract 80 million tonnes of local limestone, it would appear to have a lengthy future.

Figure 5.5 Visual and atmospheric pollution at the Hope Valley cement works

Review

8 With reference to the Hope Valley cement works case study, suggest ways in which the level of visual pollution might be reduced.

9 Which of the three different types of aesthetic pollution do you think most threatens the environment? Justify your viewpoint.

10 In what ways does aesthetic pollution differ from chemical pollution of the environment?

11 What examples of aesthetic pollution are there in the area where you live?

1   There are many examples of how attempts to solve one environmental problem simply create another. Research the conflicting environmental impacts associated with creating tidal power by means of a barrage across a major estuary (e.g. the Severn or Mersey).

2   How adequate are the current measures taken to protect areas of high landscape quality and conservation interest from development and despoliation?

3   The main instruments for maintaining and enhancing areas of high landscape quality in the UK are the designated National Parks, Areas of Outstanding Natural Beauty (AONBs) and Heritage Coasts. Find out more about these special areas: what are their aims, and how are they managed?

4   Using bi-polar analysis techniques, carry out an Environmental Quality Survey along a transect from a town or village centre towards its periphery. How many of your quality criteria would be classified as 'aesthetic' qualities? Where are the areas of highest and lowest environmental quality? What factors appear to influence their distribution?

6

Regimenting rivers

The natural system

Nowhere is the interface between people and the physical environment seen more clearly than in the context of river systems and human attempts to manage and control them. The physical processes operating in a river system are governed by several environmental factors. These include:

- the size and shape of the drainage basin
- the amount and type of precipitation received by the drainage basin, when it falls and its intensity
- the nature of the bedrock and soils of the catchment area and the amount of infiltration and throughflow that these permit
- the types of vegetation cover and their extent
- the amount of modification of the river basin by human activities.

As water in a river makes its way downstream, it expends energy on erosion, transportation and deposition of materials in its channel and floodplain. In their natural state, river channels vary widely in character. Channel size and form are both strongly influenced by peak discharge. These in turn affect the speed with which sediments are eroded and transported. Unmodified rivers and their floodplains are in **dynamic equilibrium**. They are continuously adjusting to accommodate changes in discharge and sediment load. So long as there are no sudden changes to those inputs and outputs, the components of the river system remain fairly stable (**6.1**). Many of the catastrophic floods experienced around the world during the 20th century can be blamed on human actions that have in one way or another disturbed the dynamic equilibrium. These include the deforestation of catchment areas and the draining of floodplains for agriculture, industry and housing.

Figure 6.1 The drainage basin as a system

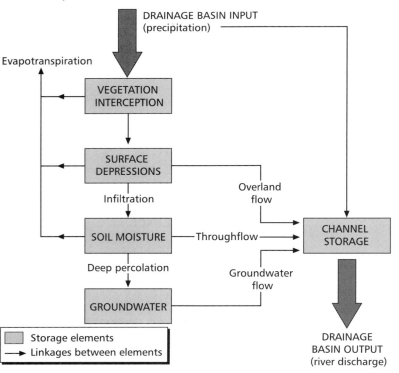

More recently, the advent of global warming is adding to the risk and incidence of flooding.

Case study: Changes in the Ganges –Brahmaputa catchment

The Ganges–Brahmaputra drainage basin in Bangladesh is an example of a densely populated, low-lying area that has been severely affected by mismanagement of its catchment area. Forest clearance in Nepal has rapidly increased runoff rates and the intensity and frequency of flooding. Snowmelt in the Himalayas and heavy monsoon rains cause flash flooding, especially when the peak discharges of the Ganges and the Brahmaputra coincide. The rivers soon breach or overtop their embankments, submerging extensive areas of floodplain. The floods carry huge amounts of silt, which is deposited on the fields and then on the beds of the rivers themselves as the floods recede. Thus natural levées are formed and deposition on the riverbeds raises them above the level of the surrounding floodplains. This further increases the likelihood of future floods occurring. Almost every year there is serious flooding in Bangladesh. Many lives are lost, livestock and crops are destroyed and property damaged.

Review

1 Explain what is meant by **dynamic equilibrium** in the context of a river basin.

2 Why do people settle in hazard-prone areas such as floodplains?

SECTION B

A long history of intervention

Rivers have always played an important role in the lives of people, and the modification of river basins has a long history. Large rivers and their untamed floodplains have been major obstacles to migration and the expansion of territory. Equally, floodplains and deltas, like those of the Tigris–Euphrates, the Nile and the Indus, have provided fertile alluvial soils and acted as cradlelands of civilisations. Of course, as permanent settlements prospered in these areas, so began the human processes of preventing flooding, draining floodplains and abstracting water for domestic use and irrigation. As rivers became important arteries for population movement, transport and trade, so critical points along them, such as the head of navigation, bridging and fording points, became the focus of routeways and ideal locations for the growth of towns and cities. Where the water flowed swiftly, or a dam could create a head of water, rivers were exploited as sources of energy, turning wheels to mill flour or to provide power for hammers and bellows in ironworks. Every single one of these human uses of rivers and their floodplains has had an impact on the dynamic equilibrium of the river basin.

Today, people modify rivers and the land that surrounds them in many ways.

■ Channels are straightened, deepened and embanked to reduce the risk of flooding and to improve navigation.

- Floodplains are drained to increase the area available for cultivation and urbanisation.
- Water is abstracted from river channels and aquifers for irrigation, industrial and domestic water supplies.
- Dams and reservoirs are constructed for water storage and HEP schemes.
- Vegetation is cleared and the land use of catchment areas changed.
- Water is polluted by sewage and industrial effluents and by agricultural runoff.

In lowland England today, most major rivers such as the Trent, Great Ouse and Thames have been extensively dredged, straightened and embanked for flood protection and navigation. Surrounding areas have been drained and there are large urban areas of tarmac and concrete surfaces, and underground conduits. More rapid surface runoff has implications for what happens downstream. River management leads to high peak flows, increased channel velocities and reduction in over-bank flooding in average years. But under abnormal conditions, they actually increase the risk of serious flooding. Embankments that can cope with less severe circumstances may be breached or overtopped causing unexpected, severe flooding of the adjacent area with widespread damage and devastation.

Case study: Flooding in the Midlands

During Easter 1998, large areas of eastern England and the Midlands experienced severe flooding. A total of 75 mm of rain fell in 36 hours (about 6 weeks' worth of 'average' rainfall for this area) on land already saturated by several weeks of wet weather. This caused rivers to flash-flood, rising twice as fast as normal, and reaching levels higher than any previously experienced. The Warwickshire Avon, the Nene, Cherwell and Great Ouse burst their banks, inundating factories, housing estates and caravan sites located in their floodplain areas. Five people died, and 4200 properties and thousands of hectares of farmland were affected. Northampton and Leamington Spa were especially badly hit.

The Environment Agency (EA), which exercises a general supervisory role in all matters relating to river flood defences in

Figure 6.2 Flooding in Leamington Spa

England and Wales, was severely criticised for failing to cope with the problem, and for providing too little warning to local residents. The EA explained their failure as being due, in part, to the exceptional weather conditions. Such high river levels had a provisionally estimated occurrence of once in 150 years. It was also due to the amount of building that had been permitted in the floodplain areas, and land use changes leading to rapid surface runoff.

Flood defences are now being raised at low points in embankments that were overtopped and a much improved early-warning system introduced, with flood wardens and self-help groups (warned by automatic voice messenger systems), sirens and media broadcasts. The EA also recommends that further development on floodplains should be severely curtailed.

River hydrographs show the amount and duration of a river's discharge over a given period of time (**6.3**). Annual hydrographs will show how human modifications of drainage basins can change seasonal flow patterns. Flood hydrographs for individual flood events show that 'managed' rivers have discharge rates with shorter **lag-times** between the rain falling and peak discharge. In other words, rivers become more 'flashy', with higher rates of peak discharge, shorter lag-times and steeper falling limbs. This is due to rapid surface runoff from unvegetated farmland and impermeable urban surfaces, and less interception by vegetation.

Figure 6.3 Annual hydrographs for **(a)** a river with a natural floodplain and **(b)** an intensively engineered river

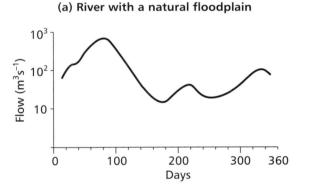

(a) River with a natural floodplain

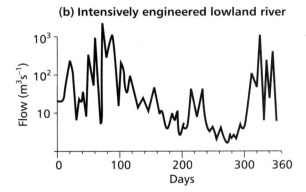

(b) Intensively engineered lowland river

Case study: Maidenhead, Windsor and Eton flood alleviation scheme

Since the Second World War there have been many land use changes in the Thames valley. While some activities, such as pumping the water-table for public water supply and spray crop irrigation, have reduced the overall discharge of water in the river, others have made its flood hydrograph more 'flashy'. Water meadows and fields have been drained, woodland cleared, new housing and industrial estates built, and part of the M4 motorway runs along its floodplain. These changes have all increased the amounts and rates of runoff reaching the Thames after heavy rain. Serious flooding has been experienced on several occasions in the Maidenhead area, making an alleviation scheme necessary.

Such schemes can be extremely costly. The 11 km flood relief channel, due to be completed in 2001, will cost £79 million (**6.4**). The Thames Water Company, which is responsible for the scheme, had to overcome many engineering difficulties. Using advanced technology, the relief channel was dug beneath the M4 motorway and a major railway line, and bridges constructed over it, all with minimal disruption of traffic. The water in the relief channel will create an attractive local amenity.

In the Thames valley alone there are flood defences totalling 5200 km, which have to be regularly maintained. There are a further 193 km of embankments bordering the tidal estuary below the Thames Barrier at Greenwich – itself a very costly project (see case study, pages 68-69).

Figure 6.4 Maidenhead, Windsor and Eton flood alleviation scheme

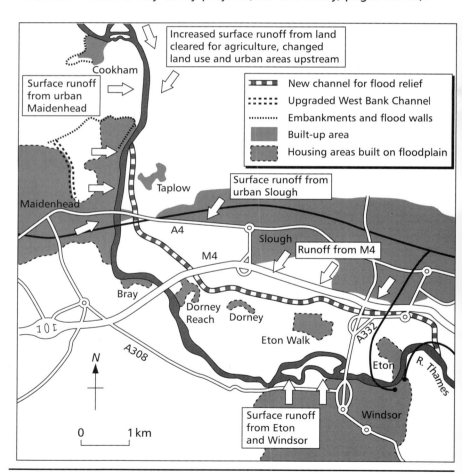

SECTION C

Towards sustainable management

In the UK, natural features of river basins, such as peat bogs in the hills, marshes, bogs and reedbeds on floodplains, have largely been drained. They have also been changed by falling water-tables, reduced river flows and, of course, by pollution. Since the Second World War, 94 per cent of Britain's lowland peat bogs have gone, along with 70 per cent of reedbeds and 60 per cent of water meadows with their lowland wet grasslands. The wildlife they once supported has also disappeared.

Where river basins have not been managed, their riffles and pools, contiguous floodplains, marshes, wet grasslands, riparian woodlands and backwaters play an important role in intercepting and storing water during and after heavy rainfall and snowmelt. They also offer a huge variety of aquatic and semi-aquatic habitats for wildlife.

- Fish and invertebrates are dependent on high water quality and on riffles, pools and quiet backwaters that provide feeding and spawning areas.
- Eroding bankside cliffs are nesting sites for such birds as kingfishers and sand martins.
- Seasonal floods and lowland wet grasslands can provide a huge diversity of plants and invertebrates, and are home to frogs and other amphibians and such mammals as otters and water voles.
- Several highly specialised bird species like lapwings, snipes, ruffs and yellow wagtails nest here in summer, while winter floods attract huge numbers of over-wintering wildfowl and wading birds.

River engineering work aimed at flood control and creation of agricultural land can have adverse effects on the ecological value of a river basin. If the river is canalised, its banks are raised and its flow regulated, so there is a loss of continuity between the river and its floodplain. An important principle in wildlife conservation is that river and floodplain should be planned together. They are integral parts of the same system. Sensitive river engineering offers major opportunities for restoring this connectivity and redeveloping good wildlife habitats.

Case study: Restoration of lowland wet grassland, Pulborough Brooks Wildlife Reserve

Most floodplains alongside Britain's lowland rivers were formerly covered with wet grassland. Traditionally, such land was used as 'water meadow', being flooded most winters and used for hay and livestock grazing when it dried out in the summer. During the 20th century, although ironically it was a man-made habitat in the first place, most of it has been destroyed

Drainage schemes, supported by government grants and the European Union's Common Agricultural Policy, encouraged more intensive use of these water meadows. They were either converted to arable use, or their productivity was raised by 'sward' improvement. The latter involved drainage, ploughing and reseeding, as well as the widespread application of artificial fertilisers, liming, and herbicides. Only 3 per cent of these former wet grasslands have been left completely undamaged by agricultural intensification.

Figure 6.5 Restored water meadows at Pulborough Brooks

Because they support large numbers of scarce breeding and over-wintering wading birds and wildfowl, aquatic mammals, insects and plants, the few remaining areas of wet grassland habitat are of huge importance for conservation. Pulborough Brooks Reserve in West Sussex covers about 170 ha of the River Arun floodplain. For centuries the flood meadows were mown for hay and grazed by cattle during the summer, but drainage improvements, including canalisation of the River Arun in the 1960s, led to an intensification of agricultural use. After ploughing, land was planted with cereal crops requiring significant applications of herbicides and artificial fertilisers. These activities had profoundly adverse effects on the bird, plant and insect life of the Brooks.

After acquisition by the RSPB and careful ecological research, a management plan was drawn up, designed to simulate the conditions that prevailed during the 19th century. The purpose is to to create and maintain ideal conditions for birds and other wetland-dependent wildlife

By manipulating water levels:

- the drainage regime has been reversed
- the area has been made wet once more, storing flood waters that disperse more slowly

- intensive growing of cereals has been replaced by wet grassland
- cattle graze once again during summer, keeping the vegetation short
- hoof-prints provide nest sites for ground-nesting birds
- dung enriches the water with nutrients when the winter floods arrive.

With the implementation of the management plan, Pulborough Brooks Reserve is now the most important area in the Arun Valley for wintering wildfowl.

Are there any other actions that might be taken to reduce the flood-risk of rivers without upsetting the system's dynamic equilibrium? The following have been suggested and are being implemented in some places:

- Generally reduce greenhouse gas emissions to decrease the risk of further destabilising global climate systems.
- Stop further building and development on floodplains and low-lying coastal areas.
- Restore floodplain areas to a more natural state to allow natural storage of excess flood water.

Review

6 What are the lessons to be learned from adopting a more sustainable and integrated approach to river management, as demonstrated at Pulborough Brooks?

Enquiry

1 Explore the consequences for river systems of changing sea-levels.

2 For a river in your home area, discover:
   a the range of methods that have been used to manage and control the river
   b what the consequences of such management have been for local physical and human environments.

3 Referring to a major river flood event, assess the extent to which human factors may have been responsible for causing the flood and intensifying its effects.

7

Controlling coastlines

The interface between land and sea

Coastal landforms are shaped by both marine and sub-aerial processes, with active erosion occurring in some places and the subsequent deposition of material in others. In their natural state coastlines are balanced systems in dynamic equilibrium.

Figure 7.1 Possible downstream effects of coastal protection

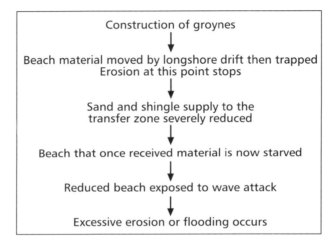

Construction of groynes
↓
Beach material moved by longshore drift then trapped
Erosion at this point stops
↓
Sand and shingle supply to the transfer zone severely reduced
↓
Beach that once received material is now starved
↓
Reduced beach exposed to wave attack
↓
Excessive erosion or flooding occurs

So long as there are no changes to the inputs and outputs, the system is stable. For example, cliffs maintain their angle as they retreat, and adjust slowly if controlling factors such as climate or sea-levels change. But human actions can often bring sudden and unintended changes that upset the natural balance. This can trigger a series of knock-on effects that have an impact on the coastal environment (**7.1**).

Case study: Unintended effects of coastal management, Minehead

Minehead is a small coastal holiday resort in Somerset on the Bristol Channel. The town has always been proud of the superb stretch of golden sands that fringe Minehead Bay.

A £13 million defence scheme was begun in 1997 after the old sea-wall was severely damaged by storms in 1995. The rebuilt wall and promenade have been raised by half a metre, with ramps and steps leading from them down to the beach. Four large groynes made of huge boulders (some weighing more than 20 tonnes) have been built out into the Bay with the intention of absorbing the force of the waves to prevent further damage to the wall (**7.2**). It is these that are the root of the problem.

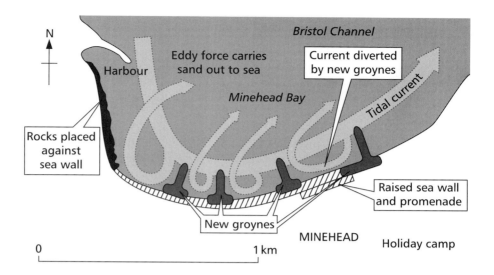

Figure 7.2 The impact of the sea defence scheme

Labels on figure:
- N
- Bristol Channel
- Harbour
- Eddy force carries sand out to sea
- Current diverted by new groynes
- Minehead Bay
- Tidal current
- Rocks placed against sea wall
- Raised sea wall and promenade
- New groynes
- MINEHEAD
- Holiday camp
- 0 — 1 km

The Bristol Channel has a large tidal range with strong currents running from west to east as rising tides are funnelled between the narrowing coasts of Somerset and South Wales. Prevailing longshore drift is also eastwards. As the tide rushes in, the groynes create huge eddies in the tidal current, and these have scoured the sand from the Bay and carried it out into the Bristol Channel. At the western end of the Bay, the sea wall and a protective embankment of rocks have stopped cliff erosion here, one of the former sources of material for Minehead's sandy beach.

There was to have been a second phase to the project – one of replenishing the beach with 300 000 tonnes of sand and shingle dredged from the bed of the Bristol Channel. This would have partially buried the groynes, and caused the waves to break further out. This would reduce the scouring effects of the tides. But at a cost of £2.5 million, the Environment Agency cannot afford to go through with the second phase. The holiday trade of Minehead faces a bleak future in the new millennium unless the funds for Phase Two can be found.

Review

1 Draw a diagram similar to **6.1** to show a systems view of the coast.

2 What alternatives, if any, were there at Minehead to deal with the damaged sea-wall?

SECTION B

Changing sea-levels

Britain's coastline has been evolving into its current shape for around 20 million years, ever since the Alpine mountain-building period. However, recent geological and climatic events have had a big impact on the shape of today's coast. Around 15 000 years ago, as the last Ice Age drew to a close, sea-levels were at least 80 metres lower than they are today. As the ice sheets melted, sea-levels rose rapidly, producing such coastal features as rias and fjords until levels became more stable again around 7000 years ago. The coastline has continued to evolve. Offshore sand and shingle bars, intertidal mudflats, spits and beaches, bays and headlands, arches and stacks are all features produced by this ongoing process.

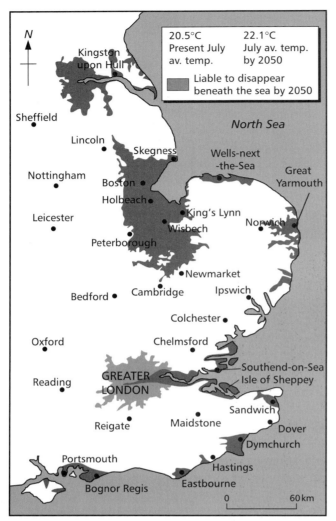

20.5°C Present July av. temp.	22.1°C July av. temp. by 2050

Liable to disappear beneath the sea by 2050

Sheffield

Kingston upon Hull

Lincoln

Skegness

Wells-next -the-Sea

North Sea

Nottingham

Boston

Holbeach

Great Yarmouth

King's Lynn

Leicester

Wisbech

Norwich

Peterborough

Newmarket

Bedford

Cambridge

Ipswich

Colchester

Oxford

Chelmsford

GREATER LONDON

Reading

Southend-on-Sea

Isle of Sheppey

Sandwich

Reigate

Maidstone

Dover

Dymchurch

Portsmouth

Hastings

Bognor Regis

Eastbourne

0   60 km

Figure 7.3 Land likely to be drowned beneath the sea by 2050

In the last few decades, presumably due to global warming, sea-levels have begun to rise more quickly once again. As the ocean waters are warmed, thermal expansion takes place, and an average rise of about 24 cm is forecast between the years 2000 and 2050. But the south and east coasts of Britain face a further problem, because sea-levels are rising relatively faster than elsewhere in the UK. Here the land will probably subside by a further 9 cm between 2000 and 2050 (**7.3**). This is the outcome of isostatic recovery in the north of Britain and a general southwards tilting of the whole country.

Case study: The Thames Barrier

In 1982, the Thames Barrier and its associated flood protection embankments were completed at a total cost of some £700 million (**7.4**). The scheme has been designed to protect London from flooding during tidal surges and exceptionally high tides. The high-water level at London Bridge has risen by approximately 75 cm over the last 100 years.

Figure 7.4 The Thames Barrier

The main threat to London comes from tidal surges when strong northerly winds cause a 'hump' of water to be formed where the North Sea narrows towards the Straits of Dover. This caused the disastrous North Sea floods of January 1953. An exceptionally high spring tide joined forces with a northerly gale to cause widespread flooding, death and destruction in low-lying districts bordering the North Sea and the Thames estuary. As the storm-driven waters were squeezed between the Dutch and British coasts, a freak tide up to 2 metres above normal levels for a high spring tide was produced.

In the Netherlands, 1800 people died and more than 70 000 were forced from their homes as the tidal-surge swept over the coastal defences, inundating the low-lying areas. Along Britain's east coast from Lincolnshire to Kent, sea walls and sand dune defences were also breached and overtopped. Canvey Island beside the Thames Estuary was badly affected. In all, 60 000 hectares of land were flooded, 300 people and thousands of cattle drowned, and 25 000 houses were damaged or destroyed.

The Thames Barrier spans 520 metres and consists of 10 radial steel gates that rest on sills built across the river-bed. These can be raised when a major surge tide is forecast. Linked to the Barrier is a riverside flood defence wall, which protects about 1000 km^2 of lowland exposed to the greatest risk of flooding. This area contains millions of homes and commercial premises.

Case study: Protecting Venice

In 1966 much of the historic city of Venice was flooded, damaging hundreds of ancient buildings and priceless works of art. The flooding was caused by a storm-driven tidal surge concentrated by the funnelling effects of the Adriatic Sea. Also responsible was the erosion of a series of low islands that formed a natural barrier to the open sea. These were built of alluvium washed into the lagoon by three rivers – the Sile, Brenta and Piave. Over 600 years ago, the rivers were diverted because so much silt was entering the Venice lagoon. The city's merchants feared that if ships could not reach the city, Venice would lose its trade. During the 19th century, channels were deepened and gaps between the islands widened. This increased erosion rates, as the area of saltmarsh that absorbed wave energy was greatly reduced. Due to globally rising sea-levels, the risk of flooding is becoming ever greater. St Mark's Square, which is visited by millions of tourists each year, is already flooded at high tide about 60 times a year, and the number of flood-days is increasing. If no action is taken, the Square could be flooded every day by 2050.

To prevent further incursion by the sea, it has been proposed that a huge steel-and-concrete barrier, many times bigger than the Thames Barrier, should be erected. It would have a series of air-filled 'flap gates' that could be raised from the sea floor when storm-surges threaten. However there is strong opposition from conservationists who regard the project as a 'short-term' solution. They point to the great impact the construction would have on the ecology of the mudflats.

In spite of daily tidal flushing of the water in the Venice lagoon, it is already seriously polluted by sewage and fertilisers leached from surrounding farmland. Every summer this causes algal blooms that kill fish and cause foul smells as the organisms rot and the biochemical oxygen demand (BOD) is exceeded. Conservationists claim that if the proposed chain of 78 steel barriers were to be built, Venice's pollution problems would become so great that all life in the lagoon would cease.

Early in 1999 the Italian Government abandoned the barrier plan, and it is now seeking to adopt more ecological solutions:

- the lagoon entrances could be narrowed
- natural accretion of silt would be encouraged
- sewage should be treated before discharge into the lagoon
- buildings should be made more flood-resistant
- 'one-way' drains should be installed to prevent tidal inflow
- embankments and paths should be raised
- a new deep-water container, tanker and cruise-ship port should be built offshore.

Nevertheless, some engineers claim that the proposed Venice barrier scheme is the only viable solution. They claim that by deciding to abandon it, the Italian Government has also decided to abandon this historic city to the sea.

Review

3 What do you understand by the term **isostatic recovery**? What is the link between this and the southwards tilting of Britain?

Checking coastal erosion

The indications are that recent climatic changes are also causing an increase in storminess. Higher sea-levels will mean deeper water inshore with more energetic waves and storm surges. Thus cliff coasts face the prospect of more rapid erosion (**7.5**). The Holderness coast from Bridlington to Spurn Point in Yorkshire is very vulnerable to erosion. The low cliffs here are made of soft glacial sands and clay, and have retreated by some 1.5 km in the last 1000 years. In 1993, cliff erosion caused a spectacular cliff fall and collapse of the Holbeck Hall Hotel. A further retreat at a rate of 20 metres per decade is expected. Cliffs at Charmouth near Lyme Regis in West Dorset are showing signs of accelerating erosion and huge cracks are appearing in cliffs at Freshwater Bay on the Isle of Wight. Many places along the Sussex coast are also experiencing active coastal erosion.

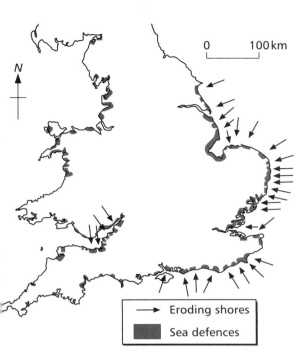

N

0   100 km

Eroding shores

Sea defences

Figure 7.5 Eroding coasts and sea defences in England and Wales

People living in coastal areas threatened by flooding, erosion and cliff retreat are demanding more protection (**7.3** and **7.5**). But as we have seen, there is strong evidence that such schemes upset the dynamic equilibrium of coastal systems. The unintended knock-on effects tend to make matters worse rather than better (**7.1**). Sea defences are expensive to build and have high ongoing maintenance costs. Some people question the wisdom of fighting what, in the long run, will turn out to be a losing battle against the sea.

Two main agencies are responsible for coastal protection in England and Wales: the Environment Agency (EA) and the Ministry of Agriculture, Fisheries and Food (MAFF) – although private owners and local authorities have a role too. Clearly, it is impossible for them to protect every metre of our coasts. Choices must be made between:

- **hard management** schemes involving expensive engineering and construction work
- **soft management** schemes such as beach nourishment or replenishment
- **managed retreat** that gives up land to the sea.

The MAFF and the EA have decided that 'hard' sea defence efforts will be focused mainly on more heavily populated areas. For rural areas a 'soft' programme of managed retreat will be implemented. This will allow the sea to flood onto selected areas of farmland. This encourages the formation of saltmarsh that slows the erosive impact of waves, and there could be also be many advantages to wildlife in working with natural forces rather than against them.

Case study: Managed retreat in the Blackwater estuary

In several parts of East Anglia, a policy of **managed retreat** is being pursued, particularly in parts of Essex. At Bradwell-on-Sea and Tollesbury, near Maldon, the sea wall beside the Blackwater estuary is being deliberately removed. This allows the sea to invade former reclaimed farmland during spring high tides. As the waves come into contact with the sloping land, friction effectively reduces wave energy. New saltmarsh and mudflats are forming, and these will provide valuable habitats for wading birds, wildfowl and other wildlife.

Hard engineering methods of coastal protection include:

- constructing groynes to trap sand and shingle moved by longshore drift to provide a protective barrier
- building sea walls and placing gabions (steel cages filled with boulders)
- providing concrete block revetments, piling and rip-rap to absorb wave energy
- creating an offshore 'barrier reef' to reduce wave impact at the cliff foot
- beach nourishment, whereby sand and shingle are brought in from elsewhere to replace that which has been lost by erosion.

Case study: Coastal erosion and defences in mid-Sussex

The mid-Sussex coastline between Brighton and Eastbourne consists of vertical cliffs of white chalk and culminates in the famous Seven Sisters and Beachy Head (7.6). The cliffs are only interrupted by the estuaries of the rivers Cuckmere and Sussex Ouse. The chalk cliffs are kept clean by constant erosion. The south-westerly alignment of the cliffs means they face the full force of waves driven by the prevailing winds. The cliff base is undercut by wave action, which removes the chalk and flint rubble after collapse. The upper face is weathered by wind, rain and frost action. Flints eroded from the chalk become pebbles, transferred from west to east by longshore drift.

Figure 7.6 The mid-Sussex coast

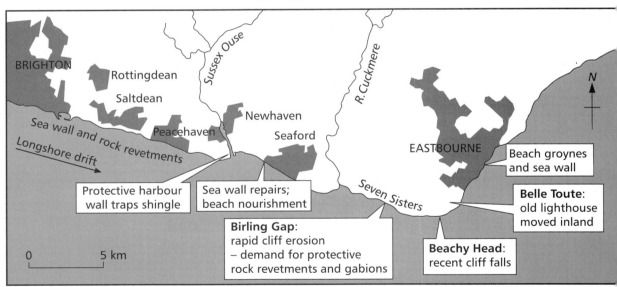

Parts of Seaford, a town of some 24 000 people, are below sea-level. It is protected from flooding by a sea wall and a shingle spit deposited by longshore drift. However, a harbour wall built at Newhaven 3 km to the west to shelter the cross-Channel ferry terminal at the mouth of the Sussex Ouse has trapped shingle and starved Seaford's shingle spit of material. In places, heavy storms have breached the sea wall and overtopped the spit, causing extensive flooding on several occasions. An extensive new coastal protection scheme has become necessary. Over £9 million has been spent on reconstructing the sea wall, protecting nearby cliffs with gabions and rip-rap, building a terminal groyne and replacing 3 million tonnes of shingle along the 2.5 km of beach. Regular beach nourishment is required, and thousands of tonnes of shingle are dredged each year from several kilometres out to sea to replenish the beach.

As if to demonstrate the rapid erosion of these cliffs, on 10 January 1999 a 16-metre-deep slab of the cliff-top at Beachy Head suddenly collapsed along a stretch of some 100 metres. Thousands of tonnes of chalk rock crashed down to the wave-cut platform below, filling in the 100-metre-wide sea channel between the cliff and Beachy Head lighthouse. It was described in the press as 'the most spectacular cliff collapse in living memory'. Days of rain and high seas pounding the cliff were suddenly followed by a hard frost. The expansion of the water as it changed to ice in joints in the rock, combined with undercutting by wave erosion, were sufficient to cause the sudden collapse.

Only 2 km from Beachy Head, at Belle Toute, an historic lighthouse built early in the 19th century is seriously threatened by coastal erosion. Although originally constructed 100 metres from the cliff edge, cliff erosion has now brought it to the brink of collapse. The answer here has been to underpin and jack up this historic building and to physically move it back 150 metres inland.

***

Decisions on the most appropriate kinds of defence to install on a particular stretch of coast have to take account of its **sediment budget**. This involves detailed studies of the physical processes involved, such as tidal currents and longshore drift and their ability to transport sediment, the sources of the marine sediments and the places where these accumulate. All these factors must also be carefully monitored after the defences have been installed, and adjustments made if necessary.

Review

4 What are the consequences for coastlines of changing sea-levels?

5 What criteria do you think should be applied when selecting threatened areas for implementation of **a** a policy of managed retreat and **b** a costly coastal protection scheme? What are the advantages and disadvantages of both types of coastal management?

SECTION D

Abusing estuaries

Estuaries with intertidal mudflats and saltmarsh are highly productive biological systems. Those in the UK are internationally important habitats for birds. They have long been subjected to human interference. Their sheltered waters are natural harbours used by commercial shipping and small recreational craft. The worms and shellfish that live in the mud, so important to migratory wading birds and wildfowl, also attract bait-diggers. The shellfish are harvested commercially. Both activities disturb the natural system.

Once salt has leached from the soil, reclaimed areas of saltmarsh can become fertile agricultural land. Around the Wash in East Anglia, the saltmarsh fringing the estuary has been claimed for agriculture ever since Saxon times (**7.7**). Traditionally, an embankment or sea wall was constructed to prevent tidal flooding, and a network of drainage ditches dug. Excess water was then pump-lifted back into the sea.

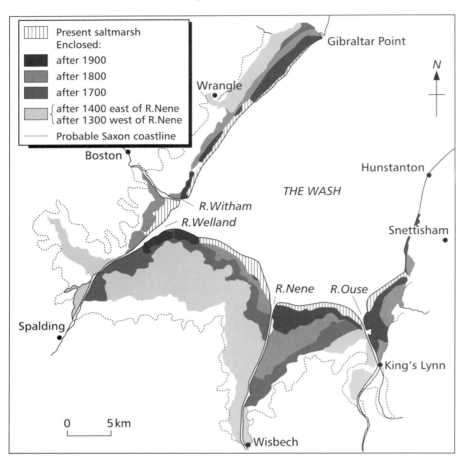

Figure 7.7 Land reclamation around the Wash

Estuaries also attract industry. Their shores, often perceived as 'wastelands', provide developers with profitable opportunities for land reclamation. The extensive flat sites are exactly what modern oil refineries and steelworks need. The fact that they are adjacent to port facilities is an added attraction. Port facilities can occupy huge areas of estuary shore, particularly where container terminals are developed. Examples include Southampton and Felixstowe in the UK, and Europoort at the mouth of the Rhine.

Tipping and waste disposal are modern methods of reclaiming saltmarsh before conversion to industrial or port development land. Examples include:

- by garbage – Belfast Lough
- by dredgings – Southampton Water
- by fly-ash from coal-fired power stations – the Medway, and the Severn near Newport, South Wales.

Estuary waters are often polluted by the disposal of industrial effluents and urban sewage.

Sailing, wind surfing and jet skiing are increasingly popular leisure activities and there is an increasing demand for mooring facilities and marinas. In Chichester Harbour in Sussex, there is a 14-year waiting list for a mooring. There are already some 170 marinas located within UK estuaries, and proposals for the construction of a further 60. They cause direct loss of intertidal saltmarsh and mud, and disturb adjoining areas.

Yet another threat to estuaries comes from barrage schemes to:

- control flooding by storm surges, e.g. Thames Barrage and the proposed scheme for Venice (**Section B**)
- assist reclamation and to create visually attractive lagoons as a focus for residential development, e.g. Cardiff Bay
- generate electricity from tidal flows, e.g. proposals have been put forward for developments on the Severn and Mersey estuaries, and a power station has already been built on the Rance in Brittany. Electricity generated in this way is 'emission free' but at the expense of important wildlife habitats. This arises because the tidal range is severely reduced and patterns of sedimentation are altered.

Case study: Dibden Bay container terminal

A proposal by the Port of Southampton to construct a new multi-million-pound container terminal on reclaimed land at Dibden Bay (**7.8**) has met with local opposition from residents and environmentalists. Although the project could create 3000 new jobs in the area, opponents claim that it will be visually intrusive, increase traffic congestion, noise and air pollution and damage wildlife.

Figure 7.8 New terminal at Dibden Bay

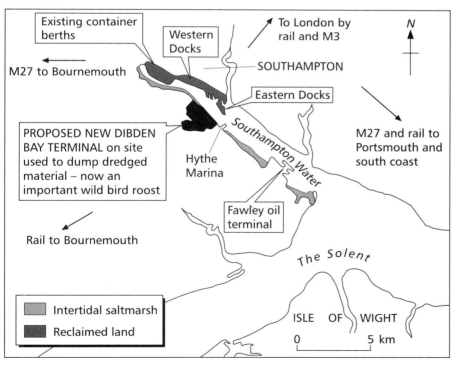

There are, of course, strong commercial arguments in favour of the project. The new super-container ships can carry 7000 containers, but there are few suitable ports available in Europe. The new development would ensure that the UK shares in this trade, with many benefits to the national and local economy. The site selected at Dibden Bay is flat, featureless land, adjacent to a deepwater channel that could be further dredged. It is a brownfield site created from reclaimed saltmarsh and mudflats on which silt dredged from Southampton Water was dumped between 1940 and 1970. If the proposed development

Review

6 Explain why the UK's estuaries are such important habitats for wildlife.

7 Set out the arguments for and against further reclamation and commercial development of Southampton Water.

goes ahead, the site will be fully landscaped and tree-screened to hide the facilities, except the tops of the container cranes that are too high.

Although the Port Authority claims that the site offers little of wildlife interest, it is used by large numbers of roosting wading birds. The adjacent foreshore of Dibden Bay and saltmarshes at Hythe and Calshot are internationally important feeding sites for migratory and over-wintering birds. It is part of the wider Solent Specially Protected Area. The new Hythe Marina Village is located at the southern end of the site. This certainly would suffer disturbance, particularly during construction. Spills of oil and other chemicals also threaten along the shipping lanes and around existing industrial plants. In the past, the saltmarshes along Southampton Water have been badly affected in this way.

Case study: Wildlife at risk in the Medway estuary

The estuary of the River Medway in north Kent is internationally recognised as an important site for wildlife. Each winter it supports over 70 000 wading birds and wildfowl. Chatham has been an important naval base for centuries, but the wide, navigable, sheltered estuary with easy access to the Thames and North Sea that attracted the Navy here in the first place is now proving to be attractive to commercial interests. Sheerness has become a busy cross-Channel ferry port, and there are several paper mills and power stations in the area. The deepwater access to the estuary is very suitable for port operations and it now handles nearly 22 000 commercial ships a year, totalling 25 million tonnes. There is great potential for further container-ship development.

The Medway's close proximity to London also makes it attractive as a recreational area, and there are increasing pressures to add to the 4000 moorings for pleasure-craft already in the estuary. The commercial shipping movements, industrial developments and high population density carry an ever-present risk of pollution, and increased problems for the disposal of waste and rubbish. In spite of howls of protest from conservationists, and condemnation of the Government by the European Court for allowing this to happen, the Lappel Bank – an area of intertidal mudflats of major ecological importance to birds – has already been destroyed.

In 1997 a new Medway Estuary and Swale Management Plan was implemented in an attempt to reconcile the conflicts between so many different interests: conservation, pollution prevention, commercial shipping, recreational uses, and fisheries. The Plan also covers land development, including the use of brownfield sites for future housing and industry. This Plan is a good example of coastal zone planning. It incorporates the principles of sustainable development and designates zones and advisory codes of practice as ways of reducing competition and conflict between the different interest groups.

Enquiry

Find out what the criteria are for designating a stretch of coastline as a Heritage Coast. Contact the Countryside Commission or consult the Internet to find some answers.

Exploiting ecosystems

The living system

The biosphere or global ecosystem consists of the physical or abiotic environment and all the living organisms that interact with it. The biosphere provides many everyday needs and resources – food, fibres, timber, fuelwood, drugs and medicines, as well as many aesthetic pleasures and recreational opportunities. Unfortunately, as these resources are exploited, so a chain reaction is started that too often ends in detrimental environmental change.

Ecosystems are ecological communities which are made up of 'assemblages' of living organisms and their immediate physical environment. Like other natural systems, ecosystems are also balanced and self-sustaining units. The **inputs** are the abiotic components of energy from the Sun, nutrients and water from the soil, carbon dioxide, oxygen and precipitation from the atmosphere. The **outputs** are the ecosystem's biological productivity (its **biomass**), oxygen and water vapour. Between the inputs and outputs lie many processes and interactions such as **photosynthesis**, the **transfer** and **storage** of energy and nutrients, nitrogen, carbon and oxygen cycling. These are vital functions found within all ecosystems.

Figure 8.1 Simplified diagram of the functions of an ecosystem

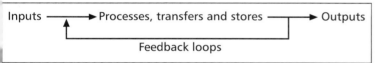

If one or more of the inputs change so will the outputs change. Through a series of feedback loops, and over time, the system will re-establish a natural stability and balance. Most natural changes are slow rather than catastrophic (except in extreme cases such as a volcanic eruption) and the system has the time to adjust slowly. Like all natural systems, ecosystems are fragile. Their balance is easily disrupted by the impact of most human activities, whether the abuse is deliberate or unintentional.

Ninety per cent of the Earth's land surface has been occupied and modified by human activity in one way or another. There are few, if any, environments on our planet that have not been influenced by people, and there is concern that the few true **wilderness** areas that do remain should be preserved in a relatively untouched state for as long as possible. Even foreign species introduced from one part of the world to another can dramatically disturb an ecosystem.

Review

1 Make a list of the ways in which you think people can alter ecosystems.

Ravaging rainforests

The tropical rainforests have for centuries supported small human populations without suffering any lasting damage. Small indigenous tribes have practised **slash and burn** methods in order to create temporary clearings in which to grow crops for a few years. This has proved to be sustainable, so long as enough time is allowed for each cleared area to recover. But when practised on an extensive scale, it can lead to a massive loss of soil fertility, soil erosion, the formation of impervious laterite crusts, climatic change and, ultimately, desertification. This has been the case in Brazil during the late 20th century following the construction of the Trans-Amazonian Highway and the large-scale clearance of rainforest to create cattle pasture.

Case study: Fire, forest and climatic change

Fire is a major factor in destroying natural and semi-natural ecosystems. This is particularly so in the rainforests. In late 1997 and early 1998, large areas of rainforest were destroyed by fire in Indonesia and in other parts of South-East Asia. Traditionally, undergrowth is burnt off late in the dry season and the fires are subsequently extinguished by the arrival of heavy monsoon rains. However, 1997 was an **El Niño** year in which the normally warm surface layers of the Pacific Ocean (about 28°C) suddenly migrate eastwards towards the coast of South America. Scientists are still at a loss to explain this phenomenon, which occurs every few years and has done so for thousands of years. This shift from the normal ocean temperature patterns brings heavy rain to the arid areas of South America's west coast, but causes a failure of the monsoon over South-East Asia. Due to the lack of dowsing rain, the fires raged unchecked. They created an horrendous smoke fog that spread over a vast area, including Singapore and much of Malaysia. The appalling visibility caused collisions at sea and the crash of an airliner.

The El Niño event continued to disrupt global weather patterns until May 1998. In March 1998, fires devastated Roraima State in Brazil to the north of the Amazon. The State has some 450 km of the Amazon Highway, along which uncontrolled 'slash and burn' has been permitted. Following one of the worst droughts on record in the area, this slash and burn activity ignited an area at least a quarter the size of Great Britain.

The Institute of Terrestrial Ecology, based in Edinburgh, claim that global warming will turn millions of hectares of rainforest into desert. Although the forests absorb and store substantial amounts of carbon dioxide from the atmosphere, rising temperatures are likely to cause further climatic change in northern Brazil and other areas that currently support rainforests. By the year 2050, decreases in rainfall of up to 500 mm per year will begin to kill forests, the Institute claims. As the vegetation decays, the carbon they currently store will be released back into the atmosphere as methane and carbon dioxide. This feedback loop will cause further change and yet more widespread ecosystem destruction.

Review

2 Explain the link between rainforest loss and climatic change.

Assaulting savanna areas

There are many other examples of fragile ecosystems that are the subject of human abuse. The Kruger Park and Gran Chaco examples below demonstrate how many areas of tropical savanna have been affected.

Case study: Kruger National Park, South Africa

Figure 8.2 Wildlife on the African savanna

Although the Kruger National Park in South Africa has enjoyed over a hundred years as a wildlife sanctuary, this 'wilderness' faces many pressures and uncertainties concerning its future.

The habitats in the park are savanna types, covering an area the size of Wales. The park is home to an immensely rich biodiversity.

When the park was first established, the original tribesmen were thrown out of these, their ancestral lands, by the Afrikaner White settlers, in order the protect the natural wilderness. Today, over 2 million people live around the borders of the park, for the most part existing in poverty-stricken squatter camps, small villages and townships.

Since the overthrow of Apartheid, the South African Government has been challenged by the Black communities to ensure that they get their share of the economic benefits from the tourists attracted to the park. Some villagers (mainly women) have to walk many miles each day to obtain their daily water needs, yet over 500 boreholes have been sunk to provide water for the park's wild animals. The people are short of food, firewood, building materials and employment opportunities. Some communities demand that they should be allowed to reoccupy the lands within the park from which their ancestors were displaced.

Soon the South African Government will have to find a satisfactory compromise. Somehow the park authorities and local communities will need to work together for their mutual benefit and to preserve the park for posterity. Can the increasing demand for tourist facilities, safari trails, tourist accommodation and the needs of the local population be met without destroying the integrity of one of the world's last great areas of wilderness?

Case study: South America's Gran Chaco

The Gran Chaco is a huge area of some 1 600 000 km^2 of savanna in northern Argentina, Bolivia and Paraguay. It is South America's second largest biome after Amazonia. It experiences highly seasonal rainfall, and in the dry season temperatures can reach 49°C. In the past, all of the area was savanna with a rich variety of tall grasses interspersed with hardwood forest, dominated by a tree known locally as *quebrachos* – the 'axe breaker'.

Around 1880, railways were built into the area and European migrants encouraged to settle. Since then, there has been extensive timber harvesting and charcoal production, the savanna vegetation being replaced by crop production and livestock grazing over much of the area. The result today is that much of the Chaco is unproductive scrubland. As wood supplies and the availability of good grazing have declined, so the settlers have faced increasing poverty. Many have abandoned the land and drifted to the bright lights of the towns and cities.

Satellite images reveal massive overgrazing of the area, with large areas of bare, eroded ground around the cattle stations clearly visible from space. The remaining trees are struggling for existence. The *quebrachos* produces prolific quantities of seed every three to five years, but cattle and goats immediately graze-off any sprouting seedlings. In some areas, there is a monoculture of soybeans grown as a cash crop, but this exhausts the soil. The migrants – the Campesinos – came from a temperate climate, and found themselves in a savanna ecosystem that they did not understand and did not know how to manage. To add to their problems, many people today are suffering from the incurable Chagas disease, which is caused by a parasite that is spread by an insect carrier, in a similar way to sleeping sickness in Africa.

There is a strong case for managing the savanna ecosystem in a more sustainable way. As an experiment, a 10 000 ha area in Argentina, known as Los Colorados, has been fenced to prevent encroachment. Livestock are removed and the native savanna trees and grasses allowed to recover. Once they have done so, a sustainable management system is drawn up and implemented. Grazing is carefully controlled using small plots that are rotated regularly. Timber will be harvested selectively on a 40- to 50-year cycle, leaving mature *quebracho* trees to produce seed. Ecotourism will be trialled as a potential and much-needed extra source of income.

It seems that the Los Colorados management system is ecologically feasible and already showing benefits. Preservation of the natural ecosystem greatly reduces erosion and increases biodiversity. However, if the system is to be more widely adopted by the poor Campesinos and native Indians, initial subsidies will be necessary. Otherwise, the progressive poverty of the people and degradation of this fragile ecosystem seem set to continue.

Review

3 Identify the essential features of savanna ecosystems.

4 If you were asked to advise the South African Government on drawing up an action plan to secure a sustainable future for the Kruger National Park, what measures would you suggest should be included?

5 Make a case for regarding the Kruger National Park as a wilderness.

Introducing and engineering species

A key global environmental issue that is likely to loom even larger in the future is that of invasive species. People today, encouraged by globalisation and affordable transport, travel the Earth. Our pets, livestock, crops and cultivated flowers are transported too, both intentionally and accidentally, crossing oceans and other natural barriers with increasing frequency and ease.

Biological isolation has been the major factor in the evolution of the diversity of life on Earth. In isolation, different species evolve from common ancestors; special ecological relationships are built up and unique ecosystems arise. But today, 'foreign' species jump the obstacles that fostered the evolution of different species in the first place.

As introduced plants and animals, pests and diseases settle into their new homes, they seldom meet much resistance. Often they may out-compete the native flora and fauna. There are many examples. In the UK, the American grey squirrel has caused widespread damage in commercial woodlands and has almost eradicated the native red squirrel. Even the humble European house sparrow causes great problems in those countries to which it was transported by colonial settlers. In the USA, for example, there are now large flocks of these birds. They cause massive crop damage. A recent estimate suggested they cost American farmers as much as $500 million per year.

Remote islands have often developed their own unique flora and fauna. In the past, such places were usually free from scavengers like rats and predators such as cats. Unfortunately, as people explored the Earth and settled in newly discovered places, these scavengers and predators were introduced, often by accident. Such invasions have had a devastating impact on wildlife populations.

On Ascension, a remote volcanic island in the Atlantic, rats escaped from visiting ships that called there to refuel and to ship guano. Rats soon over-ran the island. Someone then had the bright idea of introducing cats to catch the rats. Unfortunately, the cats found the chicks of ground-nesting seabirds easier meat. Together, rats and cats have destroyed some of the largest seabird colonies of the Atlantic Ocean, bringing some species to the verge of extinction.

Case study: Nile perch introduction to Lake Victoria

Lake Victoria in Africa is the world's largest tropical lake. It is located in one of the most populated areas in Africa. Traditionally, the lake has provided many people with water, food and transport.

The lake's fishery used to rely on two particular species of tilapia fish, but by the 1960s these were becoming scarce. As the tilapia declined, the decision was made to introduce a new species for the table, the Nile perch. This is a large predatory fish that grows to a length of 2 metres and weights up to 200 kg.

It took 20 years for the population of Nile perch to increase significantly, but as it did the numbers of small fish declined sharply. Once there had been some 300 species of small fish and these had accounted for 83 per cent of the lake's biomass. By 1985 this figure had fallen to only 1 per cent. About 60 per cent of the small fish species had become extinct. This was partly due to the predatory nature of the Nile perch. It was also related to the fact that a rising population around the lake increased inputs of nutrients derived from human effluent. Algal blooms became more frequent, the water became murkier and there were massive fish kills. Then in 1990 another alien species, the water hyacinth, invaded the lake. This has proliferated because of the high nutrient levels. At the same time, its choking action has greatly reduced the space available for most fish.

So what is the end result? Local communities may have benefited in the short term from the introduction of Nile perch. Employment in fishing and fish processing increased; so too did food supplies. By 1995 fish had become Uganda's second most important export. However, while fish used to be the cheapest source of protein available locally, the demand from the fish-processing plants has driven prices up. Today, the cost of fish is now well beyond the means of most local people. Water quality has continued to deteriorate, and the Lake's ecosystem has been transformed, seemingly irreversibly.

Belated efforts are being made to reduce nutrient inputs to the lake and to control the spread of the water hyacinth. But it could be yet another story of too little, too late. There is concern that even Nile perch catches could decline if water quality is further degraded and the ecosystem collapses entirely. This important contributor to the local economy may well prove to be unsustainable in the long term.

If the introduction of an alien or exotic species can cause problems for the environment, it is perhaps not surprising that there should be such widespread concern about the potential impact of genetically-modified (GM) crops. All domestic livestock and cultivated crops and flowers have come about through selective breeding. Desirable characteristics of colour, size, yield and so on have been selected and used in breeding programmes for many generations to create the food produce that we consume today.

The difference with food crops that are genetically engineered is that genes are deliberately altered, or genes from one species may be intentionally transferred into another, perhaps from a totally different kind of organism. Many believe that such genetic modifications pose a threat to both ecological and human communities. They create new fears and levels of uncertainty.

- Can the introduced genes 'escape' into wild populations giving pest species resistance to antibiotics, herbicides and other pesticides?
- Will the new crops further increase our dependence on chemicals, with adverse knock-on effects for wildlife populations and to the detriment of the environment?
- Could genetically-modified food harm human health in the same way as genetically-modified potato is claimed to harm rats?

It may well be that the gains from genetically-modified foods will far outweigh the disadvantages, but as yet the risks are not fully understood.

Case study: 'Miracle' rice and cereals in India

The introduction of new rice and cereal varieties to India was hailed as the 'Green Revolution'. The new varieties, including the so-called miracle rice, IR-8, had been selectively bred (*not* genetically modified) by international plant research institutions, as part of the 'All India Co-ordinated Rice Improvement Project'. The aim was to produce dwarf, quick-growing, high-yielding varieties, thus solving many food shortage problems in this rapidly developing nation.

The new varieties rapidly replaced local food cultures based on lower-yielding but robust local varieties of rice, millets and other cereals, oil-seeds and pulses. Thus a diverse native system of food production, suited to local needs, was replaced by a large-scale monoculture designed to meet the demands of distant markets in Mumbai, Delhi, Calcutta and other huge urban populations.

However, the new varieties only produce high yields in optimum conditions. They demand highly fertile conditions that can only be met through the application of artificial, chemical fertilisers. Because of their genetic uniformity the new varieties soon proved susceptible to diseases and pests, resulting in crop losses of between 30 and 100 per cent. The food supply of millions of people is now precariously balanced on a narrow and alien genetic base. If this can happen as a result of 'normal' crop-breeding programmes, then what are the long-term dangers of introducing genetically-engineered crops without adequate and long-term testing?

Case study: Herbicide-tolerant oilseed rape – huge advantage or environmental risk?

Many centuries of plant breeding lie behind most of the agricultural crops grown today. By selective breeding, such traits as improved yields, resistance to disease, tolerance to drought or frost, and crops that are easier to harvest and store have been produced. In recent years new techniques have been used, such as mutation via X-rays and exposure to radioactivity. The latest is a laboratory technique whereby sequences of genetic material from one organism can be transferred into another. For example, a genetic modification of maize has produced a variety that produces a toxin which kills insects that feed on it. Oilseed rape, sugar beet, soya beans, tomatoes, potatoes and even bananas can all be genetically modified. There are fears that the genetically-modified organisms are 'Frankenstein hybrids', which may damage human health and put already endangered wildlife at even greater risk.

Recently, a new variety of GM oilseed rape has been produced. A 'barrier' gene is inserted into the seeds so that the new variety can tolerate the application of herbicides based on glufosinate. Thus, all other plant life in the field can be eliminated by this herbicide, and a totally weed-free crop may be grown. This produces several advantages for the farmer but raises many concerns for the environment:

FOR	AGAINST
■ Greatly increases the crop yield.	■ Elimination of weeds means less food available for insects and birds, thus damaging wildlife diversity.
■ Makes harvesting easier.	
■ Seed produced can be guaranteed free of weed seeds.	■ Rare plants may be eliminated by herbicide application.
■ Reduces the need for other pesticide applications.	■ The herbicide-resistant gene might be transferred to other closely-related plants by cross-pollination.
■ Reduces the need for crop rotation.	■ Encourages greater dependence on pesticides and seeds supplied by a few giant multinational companies.

Review

6 Make a list of exotic plant and animal species that have had a significant impact on British ecosystems.

7 In what ways can introduced species cause problems for local ecosystems?

Valuing wilderness

Although there can be few places on this planet unaffected by human activity, it is important to attempt to preserve those few ecosystems that remain relatively untouched as **wilderness** areas. We can never know when the natural biodiversity they contain might be needed for crop or livestock breeding, production of medicines, drugs or other materials.

The remaining areas of rainforest are one example, even though huge tracts may be unintentionally affected by climatic change. Rainforests play a crucial role in maintaining the world's atmospheric balance and are important **carbon sinks**, storing the carbon dioxide emitted by burning fossil fuels and other organic materials. They also contain huge numbers of plant species. Many have yet to be identified and little is known of their potential for human exploitation. There must be international agreement to apply the precautionary principle by preserving these and other areas of wilderness that remain. Antarctica provides an example of what can be achieved.

Case study: Antarctica, the last great wilderness

The continent of Antarctica accounts for 10 per cent of the Earth's land surface. It is remote, largely covered with an ice cap, and so cold that there is almost no plant growth on land. The seas around, however, are rich in fish. All human activities in Antarctica are potentially hazardous to its fragile environment.

Figure 8.3 Antarctica – the last wilderness

Scientists fear that with rising global temperatures, the Antarctic ice cap might be melting. If at some time in the future it does melt, global sea-levels could rise by an average of up to 5 metres. The evidence is conflicting. There are suggestions that some of the ice shelves around the continent are breaking up. But a team of British scientists, who have analysed no fewer than 4 million satellite readings made between 1992 and 1996, think otherwise. The satellites bounce radar signals off the surface of the ice cap and are able to determine its thickness with great precision. The readings show that it has remained identical in thickness over that five-year period. This means that at present there is no melting or acceleration in the movement of ice off the continent.

There is no permanent human population on Antarctica, although there are teams of research scientists working at a number of bases. It is also an increasingly popular destination for ecotourists because of the spectacular scenery (**8.3**) and the immense colonies of penguins and other seabirds there.

Even in such a remote place there are now traces of pollution. There is evidence of:

- atmospheric fallout of dust and suspended particulate matter pollutants derived from faraway industrial areas accumulating on the surface of the ice

- an alarming amount of litter and debris left by visitors and research teams
- a build-up of contamination by nitrates and phosphates mainly from sewage outfalls close to the research bases.

There are also fears that increasing numbers of tour ships could unintentionally introduce viral and bacterial diseases to the wildlife of the area. In 1997, an outbreak of salmonella was found in a colony of penguins on Bird Island, and the infectious bursal disease virus, which affects poultry, has been found in emperor penguins. There is also concern about infestations of mice brought in with grain supplies and about non-indigenous grasses growing near a former Russian base.

In order to preserve Antarctica's pristine wilderness state for as long as possible, the 26 member nations of the Antarctic Treaty have signed up to the Antarctic Environmental Protocol (also called the Madrid Protocol 1998). This states that:

- Antarctica should be declared a World Park
- all research done there will be for peaceful purposes
- the continent's rich oil and mineral deposits should not be exploited for a period of 50 years
- the introduction of non-native (alien) flora and fauna to the continent is prohibited, including bacteria, viruses, yeasts and fungi
- tourist activities should be kept offshore as far as possible, with all sewage and waste disposed of well away from the continent
- researchers should take all their waste back with them when they leave the continent.

Unfortunately, the Protocol does not apply to fishing, and there is increasing exploitation of the krill and other fish stocks of the Southern Ocean offshore. Over-fishing or pollution could greatly affect bird and marine mammal populations by damaging the food chain. The long-term effects of holes in the ozone layer over Antarctica remain to be seen.

The key question, as yet unanswered, is: 'Who will responsible for monitoring the agreement?'

Review

8 Suggest a definition of **wilderness**.

9 What are the moral dilemmas faced by the human population in making decisions concerning **a** the exploitation and **b** the conservation of wilderness areas?

10 Why is it important to retain Antarctica as a pristine wilderness for as long as possible?

Enquiry

1 Are genetically-modified crops the long-term solution to the world's food shortages?

2 Find out more about the Antarctic Treaty and the Madrid Protocol.

3 Should national parks be conserved as wilderness areas or developed as tourist attractions and living zoos?

9 Countdown

Making choices

How we choose to live and the way we treat our fragile environment really do matter. It is all too evident that people, deliberately or unintentionally, have imposed many undesirable and often unexpected changes. Frequently, this is through ignorance and our failure to realise the complexity and fragility of natural systems. Our slowness to realise our mistakes means that we are putting many of our environments on a countdown to complete destruction.

As humans we differ from other animals in that we have the ability to think of the future and plan ahead. If we so choose, we can slow the rate of change. In some cases, but not all, the adverse changes we have set in train may even be reversed. In most cases of environmental pollution and abuse, there is a solution to the problem, although implementation of that solution will involve costs. The **polluter pays principle** is one possible course of action. But we must all recognise that even here it will be the consumer who pays in the end, for any costs incurred by the producer will be passed on. Perhaps this is not so unfair as it might seem at first sight. After all, it is the consumer who has created the demand that eventually instigates the act of environmental degradation by the product's manufacturer.

Predictions made about future environmental changes, and the models on which they are based, are still very imprecise. For example, there is still disagreement about the amount of change we can expect from global warming and sea-level rises. Part of the problem is that any alteration of the fragile balance of the environment can trigger a cascade of other effects, as the simplified diagram of some possible effects of global warming demonstrates (**9.1**).

Many environmentalists advise restraint and the adoption of the **precautionary principle**. If it is suspected, for example, that the use of any particular chemical has the potential to damage the environment, then it should not be used until more is known about its effects. There are similar concerns about the unknown effects on the environment of using **genetically-modified crops**, and the major environmental organisations in the UK advise a moratorium on their introduction. Better to be safe than sorry!

Ideally, every citizen on this planet should want to care for the environment and feel the motivation to do so. In practice, however, many people simply cannot be bothered and seem not to care what the future has

Figure 9.1 The cascade of events following the greenhouse effect

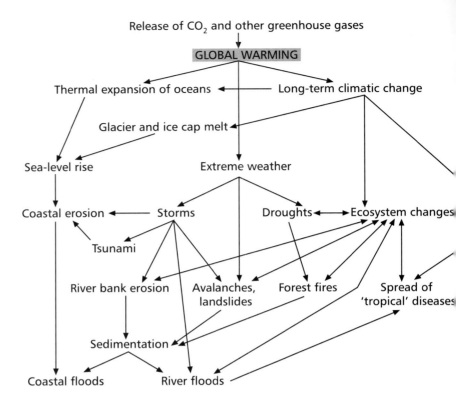

in store. In some poorer countries, where existence is so often hand to mouth, people may feel they have no choice but to abuse the environment. Faced with drought and starvation, desperation will determine how people behave. They probably realise they are destroying their own future by cutting down a tree, but unless their livestock eat the leaves, they will die. They will have no future anyway.

Clearly, air pollution is causing many problems for our fragile environment, natural systems and human health. Many of the sources of air pollution are to do with our production and consumption of energy for transport. In 1990 there were 486 million cars in the world. Industrial processes, domestic heating, cooking, entertainment and gadgets all use energy too. Pollution is a global problem that requires global solutions.

International agreements will need to be reached and implemented on such issues as the control of population growth, and the emission of carbon dioxide and other gases, as well as on rates of resource consumption. The global economy will need to be restructured and new policies adopted with regard to development initiatives, Third World debt and the reduction of poverty.

The industrialised countries must be prepared to change their own consumption habits and to find alternatives to fossil fuels. There is an increasing commitment to developing renewable sources and towards greater energy efficiency. At the present time, the less-developed part of the world consumes a relatively small proportion of the world's energy and resources, but it accounts for a huge proportion of the human population. Between them, India and China account for 40 per cent of the world's population, and both are engaged in rapid drives for development and industrialisation. The material benefits from such growth will hopefully help to eliminate unemployment, disease and poverty. But the implication is that their demand for material goods will rapidly increase. This will result in a far greater use of energy and, of course, a rise in pollution and carbon dioxide emissions. Should the MEDCs be prepared to transfer technological know-how and provide the investment capital to allow the LEDCs to develop in more sustainable ways?

Even the LEDCs are now producing more hazardous and toxic waste than they can safely dispose of within their own territories. As pollution controls and enforcement in many of those countries are weaker than those in the MEDCs, there is an increasing tendency for less than scrupulous companies to participate in a lucrative North–South shipment of toxic waste. There have been recent attempts, such as by the Basel Convention of 1995, to control the movement of hazardous wastes across international boundaries, but many countries have yet to ratify the agreement. To get around the ban, many 'waste export' schemes are claiming that the materials being exported have some further use or are for recycling. Both excuses are accepted by the Convention. The export of used car batteries from the USA to Brazil for recycling is an example. Recovery of the lead from the battery plates might be highly desirable from many economic points of view, but it has a terrible impact on the health and environment of the local people.

Case study: Hazardous ship-breaking in India

In Gujarat, in north-west India, the Alang Ship-breaking Yard employs some 40 000 casual labourers to strip steel from obsolete ships brought in from countries such as the USA and Germany, on the pretext of recycling. This provides a cheap source of scrap-iron for India's steel industries.

At first sight, this recycling would seem to be making a useful contribution to the sustainable use of resources and environmental protection. However, the rusting vessels being broken up have often been used for transporting hazardous substances such as asbestos, lead and PCBs. The yard's workers, many of whom are migrants from other parts of India, work in the most appalling and hazardous conditions for very little pay. With no more protection than a neck-scarf tied over the nose, the workers experience exposure to life-threatening toxins, and there are frequent accidents. In 1997 one ship at the site exploded, causing 50 deaths. Another, in 1998, killed five people. The frequent incidence of death by poisoning is not regarded by the managers of the Yard as serious enough to be recorded.

1 What do you understand by **a** the **polluter pays principle** and **b** the **precautionary principle**?

2 Weigh up the arguments for and against the recycling of ships. What are the alternatives?

While some argue that there should be an immediate blanket ban on all such hazardous hulks, the owners of the yard and some industrialists in India see such demands as a ploy to stop their own economic growth – environmental concerns are merely used as the excuse. Their's is perhaps a valid argument – better to dismantle these redundant ships than leave them rusting in shallow waters or sinking them at sea.

In any case, it is unlikely that vessels of the kind being broken up here would be covered under the terms of the Basel Convention. The demand for cheap steel in LEDCs is such that the practice is likely to continue for the foreseeable future, with all the attendant risks to workers as well as to the environment. As far as the original owners of such ships are concerned, out of sight is out of mind.

SECTION B

From abuse to sustainability

The concept of **sustainable development** was first introduced by the World Conservation Strategy in 1980, and was subsequently refined by the Brundtland Report of 1987 and by the Earth Summit on Environment and Development held in Rio de Janeiro in 1992. If degradation of the fragile environment is to be minimised, and the consumption of non-renewable resources reduced, then all of us will have to make dramatic changes to our life-style.

Major shifts in attitude are needed, but how can such shifts be achieved? A wide range of instruments may be used. On the one hand, there is the 'big stick' approach of insisting that everyone must conform. This may involve legislation. If the laws are strictly imposed, with heavy fines and penalties such as imprisonment for breaking the law, then organisations and individuals have no option. They will have to behave in particular ways for the sake of the environment. On the other hand, there is willing, voluntary participation in moves towards sustainability. People come into line because to them caring for the fragile environment makes sense. Between these two extremes, there are many other actions, some of which involve 'carrots' or 'sweeteners' in the form of compensatory payments and incentives (**9.2**).

Figure 9.2 Different attitudes to solving environmental problems

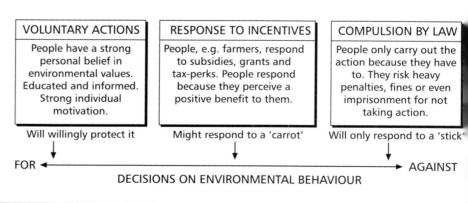

VOLUNTARY ACTIONS	RESPONSE TO INCENTIVES	COMPULSION BY LAW
People have a strong personal belief in environmental values. Educated and informed. Strong individual motivation.	People, e.g. farmers, respond to subsidies, grants and tax-perks. People respond because they perceive a positive benefit to them.	People only carry out the action because they have to. They risk heavy penalties, fines or even imprisonment for not taking action.
Will willingly protect it	Might respond to a 'carrot'	Will only respond to a 'stick'

FOR ← → AGAINST

DECISIONS ON ENVIRONMENTAL BEHAVIOUR

There is thus a range of solutions to environmental problems:

- enforced legislation with heavy penalties imposed by governments at local, national and even international levels; e.g. in the USA, pollution-producing industries now face multi-million-dollar fines for continuing to pollute the environment – a similar system of fines for environmental pollution could be applied in the UK in the future
- international agreements, treaties and protocols
- special-area designations with in-built planning controls
- financial incentives in the form of compensatory payments or penalties
- adoption of voluntary codes of practice
- personal actions taken by informed and motivated individuals, groups and voluntary organisations
- more programmes of environmental education to encourage attitudes that care for the environment.

Let us return for the last time to Delhi with its many pollution problems, some of which we have looked at in earlier chapters. What is being done here to tackle the problems?

Case study: Delhi's 'Operation Clean-up'

Despite the obvious connections between the badly polluted environment and damage to human health, it is difficult for Delhi's authorities to know where to start in reducing the problems, but some attempts are being made through 'Operation Clean-up'. This aims to:

- reduce exhaust emissions by encouraging more use of public transport and better vehicle maintenance (many people travelling to work now wear smog-masks)
- introduce and implement stricter controls on vehicle noise, with heavy fines for offenders
- establish and set low-noise targets for 'silent zones' in residential areas of the city
- improve drainage, sewage disposal, sanitation and water quality
- increase public awareness of personal hygiene, health and environmental issues through educational programmes
- encourage the relocation of polluting industries currently within residential areas
- fine heavy industrial polluters who blatantly ignore standards laid down nationally.

But there is a long way to go. A look at the figures for the number of vehicles per kilometre of road shows that Delhi has one of the highest figures in Asia (9.3). One answer to the traffic congestion problems that contribute so much to Delhi's pollution must be better management of the road space available: for example, easing traffic flows with roundabouts and traffic filter systems. A better system of public transport would also help to reduce the use of the motorised rickshaws, which are both slow-moving and heavy polluters.

Figure 9.3 Traffic congestion in Delhi is a cause of pollution

We have suggested that many environmental problems are international, and that they therefore require international solutions. This can have major implications for many overseas aid and development projects. A problem with many 'traditional' projects has been that conservation and environmental protection have not been central objectives. Rather they have been put in as an after-thought, with little, if any, budget for their implementation. They have also been 'top-down', in that they have been introduced by governments with little regard for the needs and knowledge of local people and their immediate environment.

So how can the conflict between growth and environmental protection be reconciled? One priority might be to make Environmental Impact Assessments integral to all major development projects. They should not just weigh up the likely impacts of a particular project, they should also look at alternatives, so that informed decisions can be made. There should also be participation in the assessment process by all the **stakeholders** (i.e. all who are likely to be affected) and in the decision-making process. In other words, the approach needs to be bottom-up rather than top-down.

Review

3 Write your own definition of **sustainability**.

4 Explain the difference between a top-down and a bottom-up approach to environmental problems.

SECTION C

Thinking globally, acting locally

The fact has been stressed throughout this book that all aspects of the environment are interrelated. Thinking globally is highly desirable, but most action in the fragile environment takes place in a local context. Environmental issues do not exist in isolation from the local community, nor can they be tackled in isolation. The sheer magnitude of problems such as air pollution and the greenhouse effect, together with the proper management of rivers, coasts and ecosystems, can be daunting, but individual actions taken locally all add up.

By our actions, we the human race have upset the natural balance and disturbed the dynamic equilibrium that has taken millions of years to evolve. By our actions, we have allowed many species of plants and animals to become extinct. Initially, this was through the hunting and collecting of rare species, but increasingly it has resulted from the introduction of new species, the changing of habitats and the creation of rising levels of environmental pollution. We need to ask ourselves: If we are making the world increasingly uninhabitable for plant and animal life, how much longer will it be before it becomes uninhabitable for us? So long as the well-being of the fragile environment hangs in the balance, so too does the future of the human race.

Enquiry

1   Find out more about the Basel Convention of 1995. Does it provide a proper basis for the control of international dumping of toxic and polluting wastes? What other examples are there of international initiatives to control pollution?

2   What actions are being taken in your local community to care for the environment in a more sustainable way?

3   a What are the main government departments and voluntary organisations responsible for wildlife conservation in the UK?
    b For one of these organisations, write a short essay on its particular role and responsibilities.

4   What were the international agreements, now known as Agenda 21, reached by world leaders at the Earth Summit on Environment and Development held in Rio de Janeiro in 1992? How far have these agreements been implemented?

Glossary

Acid deposition/Acid rain – the fallout of acid-forming substances from the atmosphere onto the Earth's surface. Acid rain (rain with a pH of less than 5.6) is one form of acid deposition, formed when acid-forming gases or particles dissolve in rainwater. Most acid-forming chemicals come from polluted air.

Aerosols – minute dust particles or droplets suspended in the atmosphere.

Albedo – the amount of incoming radiation from the Sun reflected by the Earth's surface and atmosphere. Ice and snow, clouds and dust particles all have reflective surfaces.

AMD – acid mine deposition: occurs when bacteria in water oxidise iron sulphide minerals in the rocks of abandoned mines. This produces sulphuric acid that dissolves toxic chemicals such as lead and arsenic.

AONBs – Areas of Outstanding Natural Beauty.

Aquifer – a layer of porous or permeable rock that stores groundwater.

Biodiversity – the variety of life on Earth or in any particular area: the profusion of plant and animal species, variability within a species and diversity of ecosystems.

Biomass – the amount of plant and animal matter present in a given area, usually expressed as dry weight per square metre.

Biome – a major global vegetation zone such as the tropical rainforest.

BOD – biochemical oxygen demand: a measure of the demand for oxygen that is dissolved in water. Demand for oxygen is very high in warm weather and when organic materials decay. If the demand exceeds the amount of oxygen available it will cause the death of fish and other aquatic organisms.

Brownfield sites – derelict land that was formerly used by housing, industry or open-cast quarrying. It is often contaminated by toxic chemicals.

Carbon tax – a tax imposed on the fossil fuels proportional to the amount of carbon dioxide produced when a particular fuel is burned.

CFCs – chlorofluorocarbons: chemicals that were formerly used as the propellant in aerosol spray cans, as a coolant in freezers, refrigerators and air conditioners; and in the manufacture of polystyrenes used for fast-food packaging. The chlorine in CFCs is responsible for damaging the ozone layer in the stratosphere.

Ecotourists – tourists who visit an area to enjoy its wildlife and environmental interest.

Eutrophication – enrichment of water by nitrates and phosphates. Increased enrichment, e.g. by runoff of artificial fertilisers, can cause excessive growth of algae and other plant life. When these plants die their decay increases the BOD, and may result in the death of fish and other aquatic creatures.

Genetically-modified (GM) crops – the result of plant-breeders inserting sequences of genetic material from one organism into the seeds of another to introduce new characteristics, e.g. resistance to insect attack or to specific herbicides.

Greenfield sites – rural land that may currently be in agricultural use but could be developed for housing or industry. Many such sites are protected by greenbelt legislation.

Greenhouse effect – the process by which some gases in the atmosphere (such as carbon dioxide and methane) behave like glass in a greenhouse, allowing solar radiation to pass through to the Earth's surface but trapping the outward emissions of radiated heat. This may be leading to global warming.

LEDCs – less economically developed countries.

MEDCs – more economically developed countries.

MNEs – multinational enterprises.

NIMBY – a person who objects to a development proposal because it may adversely affect the quality of their local environment. It is based on the phrase 'Not In My Back Yard', used to describe the attitude of the protester.

NVZs – Nitrate Vulnerable Zones: areas designated by Government as being at high risk of groundwater contamination from agricultural nitrate applications (formerly called Nitrate Sensitive Areas, or NSAs).

pH value – a way of expressing how acidic or alkaline a liquid is. It is a measure of the concentration of positively-charged hydrogen ions in a solution on a logarithmic scale. A pH of 7 is neutral; lower values are acidic and values above pH7 are alkaline.

Salinisation – occurs in the upper horizons of soils when salts rise to the surface and are concentrated by evaporation, and in groundwater when sea water replaces fresh water in an aquifer.

SPM – suspended particulate matter: dust particles of carbon, pollen etc. suspended as aerosols.

SSSIs – Sites of Special Scientific Interest: designated as areas to be conserved.

Sustainability – maintaining or conserving the resources of an area or the planet so that the needs of future generations will also be met.

Symbiosis – is said to occur where two or more species share a mutually beneficial interrelationship.

Vermiculture – the use of worms to convert organic material to compost. It is particularly effective in warm climates where high temperatures speed the processes of decay.

VOCs – volatile organic compounds, for example hydrocarbons (oil-based products) that may evaporate at normal daytime temperatures.

Zooxanthellae algae – algae that live in a close symbiotic relationship within coral polyps. They manufacture food for the living coral by photosynthesis

Further reading and resources

There are frequent articles providing the latest information about environmental issues published in such journals as *New Scientist, New Internationalist, Newsweek, Farmers Weekly, Ecology* and *The Economist*. It is also worth checking the publications of conservation organisations, for example the RSPB, the National Trust, the Wildlife Trusts, the Worldwide Fund for Nature, Friends of the Earth, and Greenpeace. Remember, however, that publications from issue-based organisations take a particular viewpoint. You may need to counter-balance these by reading the publications of particular industries and unions such as the National Farmers Union, and government organisations such as English Nature, the Environment Agency, the Ministry of Agriculture, Fisheries and Food, Department of the Environment, Transport and the Regions.

An excellent international perspective can be obtained from the publications of IUCN (The World Conservation Union). Useful information and comment is often made on current issues by the more serious newspapers including *The Times, The Guardian, Financial Times* (especially its periodic national surveys and supplements), *The Independent* and *The Daily Telegraph*.

The Internet can be extremely helpful. Each of the organisations listed above has its own website, with the latest news and viewpoints on topical issues. it is also worth searching under key words or phrases. For example, there are many pages of information from diverse sources if you search under 'global warming' or 'water pollution'.

Some book references include:

M. Witherick *et al., Environment and People*, Stanley Thornes (Publishers) Ltd, 1995.

David Elcome, *Natural Resources, Their Use and Abuse*, Stanley Thornes (Publishers) Ltd, 1998.

Simon Ross, *Natural Hazards*, Stanley Thornes (Publishers) Ltd, 1998.

K. Pickering and L. Owen, *An Introduction to Global Environmental Issues*, Routledge, 1998.

W. J. Sutherland and D. A. Hill, *Managing Environments for Conservation*, Cambridge University Press, 1996.

Survey of the Environment (annual publication by *The Hindu*, a daily newspaper in India).